Cheshire Cheese and Farming
in the North West in the
17th & 18th Centuries

CHARLES F. FOSTER

Cheshire Cheese and Farming in the North West in the 17th & 18th Centuries

ARLEY HALL PRESS

© 1998 Charles F. Foster
© 1998 James Barfoot – Archaeology in Part Two

First published 1998 by the Arley Hall Press, Northwich,
Cheshire, CW9 6NA (Tel: 01565 777 231)

ISBN 0 9518382 1 0

Designed by Julie Farquhar
Printed and bound at The Bath Press, Bath

The ARLEY ARCHIVE SERIES is designed to illustrate the development of the north west through a detailed examination of the lives of the people living there. The core of the study is the Arley Estate in north Cheshire, a major landowner since 1200, where some unusually detailed records have survived. The first book, see below, described the residents and landowners of four townships on this estate in the mid-eighteenth century. This second volume, based on national as well as local archives, focuses on north western agriculture in the 17th and 18th centuries. The third part will take the picture back to the early 16th century. Drawing on a large variety of archives it will describe the jobs and incomes of many Cheshire and Lancashire families between 1500 and 1800.

FOUR CHESHIRE TOWNSHIPS IN THE EIGHTEENTH CENTURY – *Arley, Appleton, Stockton Heath and Great Budworth*, Charles F. Foster 1st ed., April 1992, Arley Hall Archive Series, No 1, 88 pp., 7 maps, 5 b/w illus., 25 x 17 cm. Paperback ISBN 0 9518382 0 2. This is a unique snapshot of rural life in the 18th century. It details the lives of the residents of 8,600 acres in the four townships – from Sir Peter Warburton of Arley Hall to Jonathan Berry, a sheep shearer. Extraordinary details of these people's incomes and occupations have survived in rare tax returns, maps, rentals and deeds in the Arley Hall archives.

'An excellent book that deserves widespread attention.' *Archives*

'Contains much fascinating detail'. *Agricultural History Review*

'This is a lovely book to look at as well as to read.' *Open University*

Both these books can be bought direct from the Arley Hall Press, Northwich, CW9 6NA, by sending a cheque (to include postage and packing in the UK):

Vol 1. Four Cheshire Townships £6.95
Vol 2. Cheshire Cheese and Farming £8.95

Contents

Maps

Illustrations

List of Abbreviations

Cheshire R.O.	Cheshire Record Office, Chester
Chester R.O.	Chester City Record Office
C. S.	Chetham Society
Econ. H. R.	*Economic History Review*
J. R. U. L. M.	John Rylands University Library of Manchester
P. R. O.	Public Record Office. London
T. H. S. L. C.	*Transactions of the Historic Society of Lancashire and Cheshire*
T. L. C. A. S.	*Transactions of the Lancashire and Cheshire Antiquarian Society*
V. C. H.	*The Victoria History of the Counties of England*
W. M.	Warburton Muniment in J. R. U. L. M.

Acknowledgements

Part One of this book appeared in Vol. 144 of the *Transactions of the Historic Society of Lancashire and Cheshire*. I am most grateful to the joint editors for all their help.

For much of Part Two I am indebted to my friend James Barfoot who did the archaeology, made the drawings and took the photos. He also drew Map 1.

Three Arley farmers gave me much needed advice on Part Three. John Rowlandson is old enough to have started work when horses were the motive power on the farm and was therefore able to give me some understanding of farming before tractors. Modern scientific research has given us much more information both about cultivation and about animal husbandry. Ken Furness and Stephen Ford kindly shared their knowledge on these topics with me. I am most grateful to all three.

The two letters in Part One Section VII are reproduced with the kind permission of Cheshire County Council.

I would like to thank a number of other people who helped me in various different ways. Dr. Jonathan Brown and Dr A. D. M.Phillips read and commented on early drafts. Peter Robinson drew Maps 2, 3 and 4. Andrew Lamberton of Reaseheath College gave me instruction on the technology of cheese-making and notes on its history. Geoffrey Place introduced me to Air Commodore J. E. Mould who kindly allowed me to use his ancestor's contract. Geoffrey also gave me an introduction to his friend Edward Hogan who supplied details of the *Lively's* voyages. Margaret Panniker told me a lot about cheese presses and Peter Howell found the press at Booths Farm. I am grateful to Mr and Mrs Swift for allowing us to survey and photograph the house and buildings at Booths Farm. Finally I must thank my wife for photography, editorial assistance, typing and all those other things that only a model wife can do.

Introduction

The principal cheese eaten in London in the late seventeenth and eighteenth centuries was Cheshire. It gave its name to many eating places.
In 1678 Samuel Pepys is recorded as visiting the Cheshire Cheese
(probably the one in Crutched Friars near his house beside the Tower
of London) and legend has it that Dr Johnson and Oliver Goldsmith
often dined together in the Cheshire Cheese Tavern in Wine Office
Court, now 145 Fleet Street.[1] This essay describes how Cheshire
cheese captured a large share of the London market in the decades after
the first shipload arrived in 1650. This success brought about major
changes in the system of agriculture in the north west, in the type of
tenancy agreements and in the number of farming people.

Part One begins with evidence of the place of cheese in Cheshire
agriculture before 1650. The rapid growth of the market in London
after that date is described. The reactions of landowners and farmers
to this change are illustrated by examples of what occurred in the
four townships which formed the core of the Warburton family's
estate based on Arley Hall (Map 1).[2] From a description of the organisation of the cheese trade the analysis moves to the productivity
gains and profits made on some large farms and the implications of
these changes for the social and economic development of the whole
region.

Part Two describes a brick farmstead built by the Arley estate
between 1686 and 1690 on a newly created dairy farm of 98 acres
designed to produce cheese for London.

In Part Three the survival of some unusual archives is used to provide a detailed picture of how farming was done in Cheshire in the mid
eighteenth century. Some readers may find the numerical analysis in
this part rather heavy. The rarity of the evidence and the greater understanding of rural society that follows from such a detailed picture of
its economic base seems to me to justify the attempt. Disenchanted
readers are advised to skip lightly to the last section which gives little
biographies of a representative selection of farming people in the
second half of the eighteenth century.

The illustrations in Part Three come from a wide variety of 18th and
early 19th century printed books. They are designed to show the
general technology of farming in this period rather than particular

north western practices. Information on the sources of the images may be obtained from the publisher.

NOTES

1. *Robert Hooke's diary*, ed. H. W. Robinson (1935), entry for Sept. 1678; W. Thornbury, *Old and New London* (1873), I, pp. 119–122.
2. C. Foster, 'Four Cheshire townships', Arley Hall Press 1992 and *T. H. S. L. C.*, CXLI (1992), pp. 101–205, has maps and extensive information on these townships.

PART ONE

The development of a market
for Cheshire cheese in London
in the seventeenth and
eighteenth centuries

I

Cheshire Cheese before 1650

The place of cheese in Cheshire farming before 1650 can be illustrated from the farming in the Arley area. In the late sixteenth century the Arley estate extended over some 12,000 acres. For the fifty years from 1575–1626 it was owned by Peter Warburton, who lived in Arley Hall and farmed 500–1000 acres of demesne land around it. In his inventory more than seventy beds are listed but the number of people resident in the Hall was probably usually about half this number. He had thirty-five cows at Arley but the cheese in his inventory on 1 August 1626 was valued at less than £10, as follows.[1]

	£	s.	d.
12 cream cheese of this year's making [this is 30d. each: if they were valued at 3d. a lb. they would have been 10-lb. cheeses]	1	10	0
25 last year's 'new milk' cheese [20d. each]	2	1	8
35 this year's 'new milk' cheese [24d. each: 'new milk' meant made of full, unskimmed milk. This was the standard Cheshire cheese of later centuries. If they were valued at 2d. a lb. these were 10-lb. and 12-lb. cheeses]	3	10	0
80 Flett milk cheese [These were skim milk cheese at 8d. each. If valued at 1d. a lb., these were 8-lb. cheeses]	2	13	4
TOTAL	9	15	0

If my suggested valuations are in the right neighbourhood there were:

Cream cheeses	120 lb.
Old full milk cheeses	250 lb.
New full milk cheeses	420 lb.
Skim milk cheeses	640 lb.
	1,430 lb. = 12 cwt. approx.

This amount of cheese would represent the annual output of about

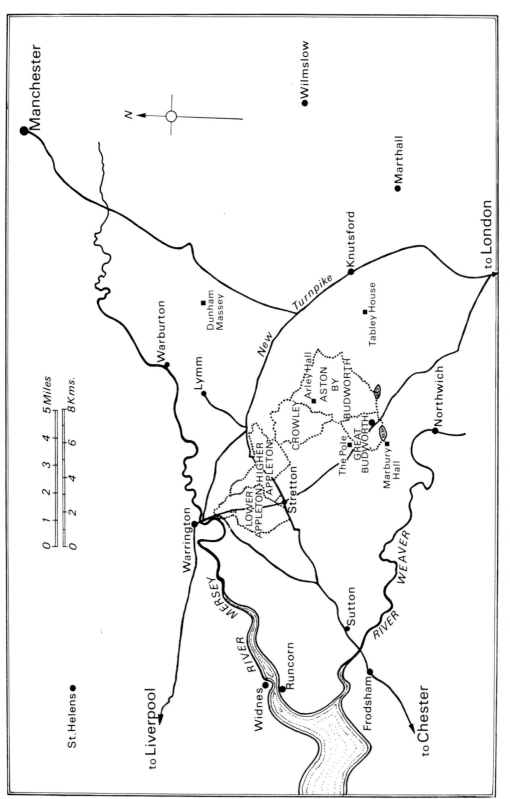

Map 1. North Cheshire in the eighteenth century showing the four townships.

six cows, so it is clear that cheese production was not the major aim of Mr Warburton's dairy. It seems more likely that this represents the surplus milk produced in the best summer months by a herd whose main purpose was to supply milk, butter and meat to the Hall. The skim milk cheese would have been eaten by the lower servants while the family, their guests and the upper servants ate the better qualities. The consumption of cheese averaged about 40 lb. a head per annum.

That no other farmers in the four townships were concentrating on cheese production is reasonably clear from a study of the twenty-four surviving inventories of farmers who kept cows and died between 1588 and 1649. In no instance is the amount of butter and cheese valued at significantly more than one might expect to be consumed by the household. The main crops were corn, meat, hemp and flax as the following two sample inventories make clear:

Thomas Ashton 3-life leaseholder of Crowley, inventory August 1639

Farm: Part of Parkmoss	£	s.	d.
5 cows and 5 young stock	25	0	0
Corn on the ground	25	0	0
Butter and cheese		6	0

George Goulden, freeholder of Crowley/Whitley, inventory November 1648

Farm: Part of Firtree	£	s.	d.
8 cows	32	0	0
7 young stock	13	6	8
Corn	10	0	0
Hemp and flax	7	0	0
Butter and cheese	2	10	0

Nevertheless some surplus cheese was undoubtedly made and put on sale at markets and fairs for the benefit of townspeople who did not keep their own cattle. In the sixteenth century, Camden tells us, Cheshire cheeses were 'more agreeable and better relish'd than those of any other parts of the Kingdom'.[2] This reputation was probably based not only on travellers' tales but on the gentry taking or sending cheeses to London.[3] One of the rare references to trade in cheese to London is to a merchant who encouraged his apprentice to start trading on his own account by dealing with chapmen who had brought goods from the north. He bought woollen stockings and some Cheshire cheeses from one man.[4] This example may well be typical because all the textiles that were brought from the north west to London came by land carriage. They were high value articles (often worth more than £50 a ton) so they could bear the high transport cost of £5 to £10 a ton.[5] If a carrier had only three quarters of a load for his cart he might sensibly have made up a full load by buying a few cheeses (at about £20 a ton). Port Books for the years before 1650 reveal very little cheese travelling to London by ship.[6] This makes it unlikely that any considerable amount of cheese went to London by land as sea freight was so much cheaper— only about £1 a ton—than land carriage.[7]

II

The beginning of the market in London and its growth

A harbinger of change was the arrival in London of the *James* of London, Robert Mills master, with 20 tons of cheese on 21 October 1650.[8] The reasons that persuaded William Seaman, a London merchant of a Cheshire family, to finance the voyage must be sought in Suffolk. That county had supplied most of London's butter and cheese from the sixteenth century and shipped them from such ports as Woodbridge and Aldeburgh. In the late 1640s this area was affected by cattle disease and floods.[9] The effect of these disasters can be seen in the doubling of the price of Suffolk cheese bought by the Navy in London.[10] As a consequence London began to buy 'full milk' cheeses from Cheshire and from the north and west of England. Suffolk had originally also produced full milk cheese but as the London demand for butter increased in the early seventeenth century, farmers had taken to skimming some of the cream off the milk for butter before they made cheese.[11] This practice slowly increased and so reduced the average quality of their cheese that by the 1660s even servants complained about being asked to eat it.[12] London cheesemongers evidently had doubts whether Cheshire cheese as a better quality product at a higher price would sell successfully, but from 1652 it was apparently shipped most years, as appears from the records of St Bartholomew's Hospital, Sandwich, Kent, near the mouth of the Thames estuary. Between

6

1652 and 1665 surviving prices from the hospital indicate a Cheshire premium of more than one penny per lb. over Suffolk cheese.[13]

The first survivor of a series of Port Books for Chester at this period shows that no less than 364 tons of cheese was sent to London in 1664. Londoners had evidently decided that the superior taste of Cheshire cheese was worth the higher price. Pepys was apparently typical when in 1660 'Hawley brought a piece of his Cheshire cheese, and we were merry with it'.[14] Throughout the Restoration period sales increased in London. The evidence from the Port Books in Appendix 1 shows that 1,000 tons a year were being sent from the north west in the middle 1670s and that this rose to nearly 2,000 tons in the 1680s. In 1689 the long war with France began and French privateers were so active that the seaborne trade in cheese dwindled and ceased altogether about 1700. In this period cheese went to London by land carriage. This increased the price by £5 to £8 a ton and seems to have slowly reduced demand (see Appendix 2 Table A and Section VII below).

In the 1650s and 1660s all the ships were despatched from the port of Chester, but about 1670 a new wharf and a special warehouse to

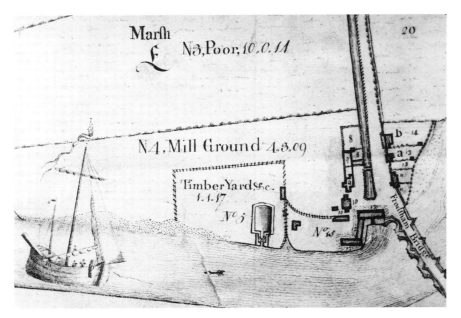

Fig 1. The port of Frodsham and a cheese ship, 1753. The Z-shaped building, No. 12, beside the bridge was the cheese warehouse. From the map of Sutton at Arley Hall.

receive the cheese were built on the Warburtons' manor of Sutton Weaver, just beside Frodsham bridge (Fig 1).[15] This was on the Mersey estuary and so within the port of Liverpool. Its trade built up rapidly and in 1679 more than 1,000 tons was shipped to London, making Liverpool at least as important a port in the cheese trade as Chester. The cheese shipped from Chester came not only from Cheshire but also from Flint, Denbigh, Montgomery and Shropshire. It was warehoused in Chester and then carried down in lighters to the cheese ships anchored at Parkgate or Dawpool.[16] The wharf and warehouse by Frodsham bridge served central Cheshire and the borders of Shropshire and Staffordshire. Farmers in the south west of Cheshire and Staffordshire could also put their cheese on the Trent. Cheese produced in Derbyshire, mostly in the valleys of the Dove and Derwent, was also shipped on the Trent. In the eighteenth century there was a warehouse at Wilden Ferry, between Derby and Nottingham, where it was loaded on barges and taken to Gainsborough and Hull for shipment to London.[17] The Frodsham bridge warehouse was probably also used for the cheese of south Lancashire and north Cheshire. The Mersey was cleared of obstructions and the Bank Quay was built at Warrington in the mid–1690s so that when seaborne trade resumed after the war in 1713 this cheese was warehoused at Bank Quay.[18] Probably only cheese from the Ormskirk area was warehoused in Liverpool itself.

In the seventeenth and eighteenth centuries cheese from all these areas was known as Cheshire cheese. This seems to have become the brand name on the London market partly because it was already a famous name and partly because during the first twenty years 1650–1670 in which this cheese was sent to London it was all shipped from Chester. With the end of the long war with Louis XIV in 1713 the cheese ships started to sail again. At least 2,600 tons a year was shipped from the north west to London in 1717 and 1718. Due to changes in the methods of the Customs and Excise, the Port Books were no longer so carefully kept after 1700 and their quality declined steadily in the eighteenth century so that such figures as do survive cannot be relied on to be a complete record.[19] The only figures that seem reliable are provided by William Maitland, who tells us that 5,766 tons of Cheshire cheese were shipped into London in 1729.[20] This shows that the market had more than doubled in size since the 1680s. The continued expansion of London's population in the eighteenth century makes it likely that it went on growing until at least 1770. From 1739 the Navy bought Cheshire rather than Suffolk cheese. In some war years they bought as much as 1,800 tons which was mostly delivered in London.

After 1750 the rise in the industrial population in the Mersey basin is likely to have diverted substantial quantities of cheese to the local market and particularly that produced in south Lancashire. At the same time the increased demand for fresh milk and butter and fresh vegetables for this new population will have reduced the amount of land near the expanding towns available for cheese production. It is likely therefore that south Lancashire ceased to be a significant supplier to London in the last quarter of the eighteenth century.[21]

The development of the canal system after 1770 allowed new areas to supply cheese economically to London. It also gave Cheshire cheese access to new markets in growing industrial centres like the Potteries and Birmingham, so the whole picture becomes too confused for numerical analysis by the end of the eighteenth century.

III

How agriculture was reorganised to supply the market

To respond to increased demand for cheese, farmers needed more cows. In the seventeenth century a cow probably produced about 2 cwt. (240 lb. = 109 kg.) of cheese a year (below), so 1,000 tons of cheese represented the output of around 10,000 cows. Dairy herds in the north west therefore must have been increased by some 20,000 cows between 1650 and 1688. To try to understand how this was done, I am going to look first at the evidence of a representative selection of probate inventories from the four townships.

Thomas Knowles of Crowley—freeholder—November 1655

Farm—Hades Nook	£	s.	d.
4 cows	10	0	0
New corn	24	16	0
Old corn	22	0	0
Hemp and flax	5	0	0
Butter and cheese	1	13	4

Thomas Knowles was a farmer who had not, so far as his inventory suggests, changed his ways. Like the two Crowley farmers we looked at earlier, he was growing corn, hemp and flax. He only had enough butter and cheese for his family's use through the winter.

John Nixon of Crowley–September 1661

Farm–unidentified	£	s.	d.
17 cows and 14 young stock	84	0	0
Hay	14	0	0
Corn	5	6	0
Cheese	26	0	0
Hemp and flax		10	0

Perhaps John Nixon is the first serious cheese producer in the four townships for whom an inventory survives. This shows a large stock of cheese—probably more than a ton—and a good stock of hay to feed his cattle through the winter. He was only growing enough corn for his family and hemp and flax have dwindled to insignificance. It is not clear which of two or three large farms in Crowley at this period was John Nixon's because he was, I think, a tenant and not, like the other farmers whose inventories we have examined, an owner. His status is interesting because dairy farming to produce cheese for the London market was different from traditional farming. It required unremitting attention to the health and well-being of the cows, combined with skill and care in making the cheese. Tenants with limited capital for whom cheese was a career were apparently more willing to devote themselves to it than richer families, and Nixon is an early example.

Edward Savage of Crowley–freeholder–March 1670

Farm–Crowley Chapel–10 acres	£	s.	d.
1 cow and calf	3	3	4
Corn	1	3	4
Hemp	1	0	0
No horse or plough. Total inventory £14 3s. 4d.			

This inventory shows that some small farmers, even if they owned their land freehold, had not changed from old style farming by 1670.

Ralph Vernon of Aston farmed on a much larger scale. There was nowhere in Aston by Budworth where such a huge herd could have been kept except on the Arley demesne. So this inventory is evidence that, as early as 1672, the major gentry like Sir George Warburton, Bt, were letting the demesne land round their houses as dairy farms while they continued living in the house.

Ralph Vernon of Aston–February 1672

Farm on Arley demesne	£	s.	d.
49 cows and heifers	155	3	4
14 2-year old heifers	16	0	0
9 1-year old calves	8	0	0
Corn	15	8	4
Cheese–4 tons	100	0	0
No hemp or flax.			

This was a significant break with the tradition of employing servants to farm the demesne to support a large establishment in the Hall. Notice that the four tons of cheese, which probably represents the whole of the previous summer's output from his forty-nine cows, was still on the farm in February, because Cheshire cheese needed to mature and harden before it would travel.

William Knowles of Crowley–freeholder–

November 1678				(Thomas Knowles) 1655			
Farm–Hades Nook	£	s.	d.	Farm–Hades Nook	£	s.	d.
6 Cows	20	0	0	4 cows	10	0	0
5 Young stock	5	10	0	Corn	46	16	0
Corn	5	0	0	Butter and cheese	1	13	4
Cheese	9	0	0	Hemp and flax	5	0	0
Hemp and flax		13	4				

The Knowleses, father and son, illustrate how farming changed in a generation. Their inventories show how a medium-sized farm was converted to produce cheese for the market in the 1660s or 1670s. But inventories seem to have survived only for the richer members of society, for perhaps the top 5–10% of the income range. Few inventories of the poorer but more numerous landowning class of three–life leaseholders in the four townships are available from this period. So for a broader view of what was going on in the whole cheese-producing area we must turn to another source of evidence.

Up to about 1700 the Port Books were kept with considerable care and the number of cheeses in each cargo was given as well as the total weight. Thus in 1664 Peter Venables shipped 3,995 cheeses which weighed 19 tons. Cheese was normally weighed in cwt. of 120 lb. (tons of 2,400 lb.) so these cheeses weighed an average of 11.4 lb. each. If we delve into the technology of the dairy we learn that 1 gallon of milk made 1 lb. of cheese, that a cow produced an average of 2 gallons of milk per day and that it was the practice with Cheshire cheese to make one cheese each day from the milk of the whole herd. So we can calculate that a 10-lb. cheese was the product of a five-cow herd and a 20-lb. cheese that of a ten-cow herd.[22]

By adding up all the cargoes each year one arrives at the following table:

TABLE 1 *Average weight of Cheshire cheeses sent to London as shown in Port Books*

Year	Average Weight lb.
1664	12.2
1670	13.3
74	17.0
75	15.9
76	13.2
78	10.4
79	10.2
1680	11.8
81	9.6
82	9.4
83	11.7
86	9.7
87	10.4
88	11.1
1690	12.3
91	12.8
92	14.2
93	13.7
94	14.6
95	14.8
99	19.4

1713 onwards: standard weight 24 lb. i.e. 1 ton = 100 cheeses

From this table and what we learnt from the inventories we can begin to reconstruct the progress of agricultural change. Commercial cheese production started on the large farms which already had dairy herds. By such simple techniques as hurrying the calves off to the butcher they could increase milk available for cheesemaking and so switch from meat to cheese production. These were mainly freeholds but the dairy herds seem to have been quite small, averaging only six cows in 1664. Until 1674 the average size of herds increased, but between 1675 and 1686 a large number of small cheeses were produced. It seems likely that these were the result of cheese production on some of the many small farms in the north west. Agricultural historians have often noticed the large numbers of farms in the area of between 10 and 50 acres.[23]

The London market would probably only take the larger cheeses, and the smaller cheeses were eaten locally or sent to less important markets. For example, on 23 June 1679 Thomas Porter shipped 2,266 cheeses weighing only 4 tons to Topsham (Exeter). These only averaged 4.2 lb. each. From 1687 cheeses grew steadily in size until by the end of the century an average weight of 20–24 lb. became standard. This implies a growth of the average herd to ten to twelve cows, which would inevitably have involved the creation of larger farms as ten acres per cow seems to have been needed in the seventeenth century (see Section V below and Appendix 12).

Before we leave the Port Book figures we can use them to obtain an approximate idea of the spread of dairying by the mid-1680s. The 2,000 tons of cheese averaging about 10 lb. each which were sent annually to London were produced by about 20,000 cows in 4,000 herds averaging five cows a herd. As well as that sent to London, much was eaten locally. For example, we have seen some 40 lb. a year being consumed by each of the inhabitants of Arley Hall in the 1620s and this was to rise to over 120 lb. a year each in the 1750s and 1760s. If we estimate that local consumption also required 2,000 tons and that about half the cows were in the county of Cheshire and half in the rest of the cheese-producing area, it would mean that there were about 20,000 cows in Cheshire. At ten acres per cow, they occupied about 200,000 acres. This would suggest that about a third of the suitable land in the county was in dairy farms in the 1680s and probably a similar proportion in the rest of the area.

Many historians of the north west have described new enclosures in the period 1660–1750 and have noticed the reduction in the numbers of small farms, but they have not pointed to changes in the markets or the technology of agriculture to account for them.[24] The analysis presented here suggests that an important driving force was the desire to create viable dairy farms with herds of ten cows or more. Both the market and the production techniques favoured this size. The London buyers preferred larger cheeses and so paid a higher price for them. A dairywoman was not fully employed with fewer than ten cows.

There were several enclosures aimed at providing these larger farms in the four townships. In Lower Appleton in the mid-1680s a large area of hilly ground where, in the Middle Ages, the Warburtons had had a rabbit warren and the freeholders had grazed their sheep and cattle, was enclosed by agreement. The ten principal freeholders received enlarged ring-fence properties ranging from 113 to 36 acres. The Warburtons acquired two completely new farms: Hillside farm of 124 acres which they let on a twenty-one-year lease at full market (rack) rent and one of 86 acres which they sold on a three-life lease. Their four principal old farms were increased to range between 172 and 48 acres. At the same period, in Higher Appleton, moss lands on the edge of Whitley Reed which had evidently been commons for summer grazing were enclosed and the lands at that end of the township re-arranged to create four large farms—Burleyheyes 181 acres (including Appleton Moss), Old farm 123 acres, Yewtree farm 106 acres, and Booths farm 98 acres, of which two were let on twenty-one-year leases at full rents and two were sold on three-life leases (Map 2).

Merging small farms together to create dairy units was easier when the land was freehold because the seller raised sufficient capital to start a new business or career. As a result of the Crown selling the township of Crowley most farms there became freehold in the second half of the seventeenth century. Surviving deeds show considerable merger activity around the 1690s with two or three farms being amalgamated into one.[25] A typical example is the 102 acre farm (now known as Garland Hall) which was created from three smaller units in the 1690s. Map 3 shows one old farm in the top left corner, the second on the right and the main unit where the farm buildings were when the map was made *c.* 1752 in the centre. As a result of these mergers more than thirty old farms in Crowley were reduced by the 1740s to seventeen.

However, the lands traditionally let on three-life leases were not so easily converted. These farms were more numerous and much smaller. In the four townships more than two thirds of the farming families were leaseholders. Their farms were typically between five and twenty-five acres; in Great Budworth, for example, on about 390 acres there were at least twenty-eight leaseholds of between four and thirty-one acres in 1700. It took much longer to make this kind of land into viable

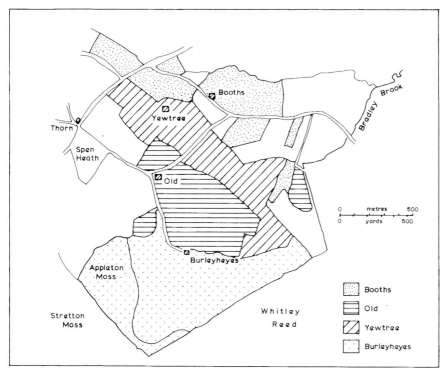

Map 2. The south east corner of Higher Appleton (now Appleton Thorn) showing the four large dairy farms created *c.* 1690 by enclosure and re-arrangement. Burleyheyes and Yewtree are compact blocks. Old has one isolated field. Booths is at least all accessible from one road. See Part Two below.

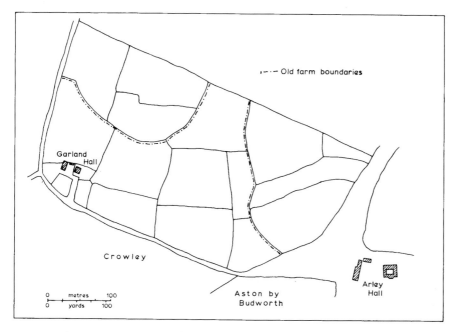

Map 3. Garland Hall Farm, Crowley, was bought by the Arley Estate in 1752 and added to the 1744 map on which this map is based. The field boundaries show the 3 earlier farms which were merged to form Garland Hall Farm.

dairy farms of between fifty and 100 acres. Here are some examples of what was done.

In Aston-by-Budworth there were two large commons. Much of one of them called Feldy Green was enclosed and divided between two adjacent farms, increasing them to thirty-five and sixty-three acres respectively. An old farm of some twenty-five acres beside Arley Moss was doubled to about fifty acres by enclosure from the moss. The marshy summer grazing bordering the Arley Brook was also divided up, giving many farms a field or two at a considerable distance from the rest of their holding. But this type of improvement still left most farms too small for dairying.

The most effective method was for some farmers to sell or let their holdings to others, and this is just what happened. The market in lease-holds in Aston in the first half of the eighteenth century was so brisk that only four leasehold families in 1749 had been in possession in 1700. One of these was the Dewsbury family, who added to the twelve acres they had held since the sixteenth century an enlarged Feldy farm of forty-four acres to make themselves a fifty-six acre farm.

Another way was for a farmer to rent land from several adjoining proprietors so as to build up an economic unit. Records of such arrangements are rare but the Warburton papers have an example in John Robinson of Aston in the 1740s. He had a twenty-eight acre, three-life leasehold at Birchbrook but was also renting fifty-three acres of the Arley demesne beside it, so he actually had an eighty-one acre farm. Next door to him Samuel Glover had built up a farm consisting of the freehold of the Reed House, Antrobus, probably about thirty acres, a thirty-two acre three-life leasehold at Hollin Hall and fifteen acres of Arley demesne, making a total of seventy-seven acres. In the late 1740s John Robinson was his tenant at Hollin Hall and probably of all this land, giving Robinson a total farm of 158 acres.[26] This example also shows how the Arley demesne was being used to help the small farmers. In addition to the four large farms, there were seven other farmers, of whom John Robinson and Sam Glover were two, whose farms were being brought up to a viable dairying size by leasing parts of the demesne.[27] The use of a further 109 acres of demesne as a 'ley' in which any farmer could graze cattle by the week during the summer gave further flexibility to the dairy farms on the three-life leaseholds. All these arrangements did evidently achieve their purpose, because although there were thirty-seven separate three-life leaseholds over five acres in Aston in 1749 averaging forty-two acres each, there were only about twenty-four farmers in 1750, who had an average of sixty-five acres each. Due to improvements in the management of cows and pastures, the land required for each cow seems to have been reduced from about ten acres before 1700 to six-and-a-half acres in the 1750s.

IV

The organization of the trade and the shipping

A seaborne trade requires ships and return cargoes. The type of ship used in the cheese trade throughout this period was the ketch. It was a manoeuvrable vessel that was extensively employed in the coasting trade. It drew 11–13 ft when laden[28] so it could take refuge in shallow bays and estuaries when storms threatened, and it had a flat enough bottom to lie upright on the mud at low tide. It increased steadily in size from 20–30 tons in the 1660s to 50–100 tons in the 1740s. It usually carried ballast to compensate for its lack of keel, so when Welsh lead required transport to London it could be accommodated as ballast in addition to the normal cargo of cheese.[29]

In favourable conditions a ketch could make the voyage from the north west to London in nine days in the 1680s, but the average of a sample of forty-three voyages in the Port Books 1685–87 was twenty-six days. In the earliest surviving *Lloyd's lists* which report sightings of

Fig 2. A ketch under sail in a river.

17

ships, the *Lyon* made the round trip from London to Liverpool and back, including loading eighty tons of cheese, between 28 January and 28 February 1741. But the *Jenkin* left London on 5 November 1741 and after taking refuge in Weymouth Bay, where she was seen on 15 November, arrived in Dublin on 1 December. In the four years 1685–89 (Appendix 3) Henry and John Thorpe were the captains who made the most voyages. They were alternate captains of one ship which made fourteen round trips, averaging three-and-a-half trips a year or 3.4 months per trip. They were more fortunate than most captains of their period, who often had to wait in the north west for a cheese cargo.

London was one of the great entrepôts of Europe. Available there were the teas and spices of the Far East, the calicoes of India, the currants and silks of the Mediterranean, the coffee, sugar and dyestuffs of the Americas, and the advanced technical manufactures—such as chemicals—only produced in the Netherlands at this period. These were the products that made up the return cargoes of the cheese ships. Such things had only usually reached the north west as the return loads of the carriers who took northern textiles to London. The expense of land carriage—at least five times that of sea freight—had inhibited this trade but there was evidently a lively demand in the north west and there never seems to have been a shortage of return cargoes for the cheese ships. This was partly because there was also a demand for goods from London in Dublin and Bristol, so that the cheese ships often called at these ports on their way back to the north west. The fact that cheese ships could easily be loaded for the return journey kept freight charges low and encouraged the trade.

The happy survival of a series of well kept Port Books for both Chester and Liverpool for the four years from June 1685 to June 1689 enables a good picture of the cheese trade to be presented. The dominant figures were the nine London cheesemongers listed in Appendix 3. Much the greatest was John Ewer, who shipped 2,741 out of the 6,613 tons of cheese recorded in these four years, or more than 41%. He shipped cheese from both Liverpool and Chester. Two other merchants, Jeremy Ives with 954 tons and Richard Halford with 870 tons also shipped from both ports, but the other six only despatched cargoes from one of the ports. As well as these nine important cheesemongers, a further eleven people shipped 365 tons between them. The reason for this hierarchy of cheesemongers seems to have lain in the organisation of the trade. Because the efficient operation of the ships required a stock of cheese to be ready in a warehouse for them to load, the London cheesemongers had soon realised that they had to employ factors to buy cheese for them in advance of the ships' arrival. Originally the factors bought cheese at fairs and markets but by this period it is likely that the practice of buying on the farm, which became universal in the eighteenth century, had been adopted. The factor would inspect each cheese in the farmer's storeroom, take samples with his cheeseknife to assess the quality, and weigh and value each cheese. When the price was agreed, the farmer carried the cheese to the warehouse. A factor could probably operate effectively within only a ten or fifteen mile radius of his home so he could ride out to visit his farmers. John Ewer's success in dominating the trade was presumably the result of having built up a complete network of factors. The merchants who shipped from only one port can have had factors only in that area.

As the Port Books show, cheese was virtually the only freight going from the north west to London. Captains and shipowners would have been unwise to take a cargo to the north west without having made an arrangement with a cheesemonger to return with cheese. This fact is reflected in the close relationships that are shown in Appendix 3 to have existed between merchants and captains. John Ewer, for example, had made arrangements with five families of captains and these families carried seventy-six of the ninety-one cargoes he shipped in these four years. If he had a cargo of cheese ready that was urgently required and none of 'his' captains was available he would evidently use whatever ship was offered. But that he took the trouble to look after 'his' captains is shown by the fact that the whole group carried only five cargoes for other merchants in the four years. Similar loyalty is shown by five of the six smaller cheesemongers, who shipped almost all their cargoes with a single family of captains.

This well defined organisation was destroyed by the long war with France 1689–1713. Although a few daring spirits continued to ship a little cheese in the 1690s, the losses to privateers in the Channel must have been too high, so that none seems to have moved that way after 1700. Instead it went by road, and the prices reflected the increased cost of freight (Appendix 2). The organisation of the market was dramatically altered. Carts and waggons carried only a ton or two at a time. It was open to any farmer to make his own deal with a carrier to take his cheese to London and hawk it round the retail cheesemongers there.[30] He did not have to deal with the wholesalers and their factors. Indeed he could take his cheese to London and sell it himself and so avoid all middlemen. See Section VII below.

Whatever happened during the war, the list of names of cheese-mongers and captains operating in the years 1713–18 (Appendix 4) is very different from the list of 1685–89. There was an almost complete change of personnel in the cheese trade. The Port Books are not sufficiently well kept to provide a more detailed analysis at this period, and we must move on to 1735–46 when slightly better information is available. The Corporation of London Cocket Book 1735–46 provides a reliable list of the ships that were operating in those years and their captains (Appendix 5, Table A). However I believe it substantially understates the number of voyages that they made and so the amount of cheese carried (Appendix 5, Table B and note 2). In Appendix 6 I have attempted to draw from the chaos of the Port Books a list of principal cheesemongers and captains operating between 1735 and 1746. This shows a substantial similarity to the 1713–18 list. It would seem likely that the structure of the trade that we saw in 1685–89 had been re-established when seaborne carriage returned. The large wholesale cheesemongers and their factors had regained their grip on the trade. Abraham Daking is said to have been the largest cheesemonger in England with annual sales of about 1,000 tons each of butter and cheese in the 1730s, and that family may have retained their dominance until 1781, when his son died by 'falling into the river as he was seeing some cheese weighed for a Government contract'.[31]

A change from the practice of the 1680s was that a number of the 1730s cheese ships bore the names of the London merchants—for example Daking, Suttle, and Homer. This seems to imply that they owned, or at least shared ownership of these ships with the captains. This would have been a desirable change because one problem for the 1680s captains had been the wait in the north west till a cargo of cheese became available. Sometimes this waiting had been so prolonged that the captains had entered into the local coasting trade and took cargoes down the Welsh coast. On at least one occasion a voyage to Ireland was made. Such waiting was clearly expensive for the ships and crews. When a cheesemonger owned a ship he had a greater incentive to organise the trade so as to eliminate this expense and keep the ship fully employed.

Other sources of information about the trade become available in the eighteenth century. Parish registers and probate records giving occupations show that cheese factors lived throughout the area that produced cheese. One of these, John Bate, who died in 1728, lived in Appleton, one of the Arley estate townships. He was one of the largest farmers in the area with about 250 acres of which half was freehold and half lease-hold. He also owned a watermill, a windmill and a malt-kiln. Other evidence suggests that cheese factors were normally substantial men of this type who had the standing in the local community to carry off the difficult business of valuing cheese and also the financial strength to make short term loans to farmers secured on their cheese.[32]

Mr Corbett Costard was in charge of the Warburtons' Sutton Wharf and warehouse between 1733 and 1766. He lived rent-free in a house on the wharf and collected the charges made for the use of the facilities. His figures for the cheese that paid 6d. a ton to use the warehouse are given in Appendix 7, which shows that between 624 tons and 1,501 tons a year paid rent during this period. He was only paid £4 a year by the Warburtons, so his services doing the paperwork for the cheese trade evidently provided most of his income. Unfortunately none of his other papers have survived but from vouchers of this period in the Warburton papers it is possible to reconstruct the likely procedure. When the cheese arrived at the warehouse he would have checked the cargo and notified the factor and the cheesemonger of its arrival. This would have enabled the cheesemonger to organise his shipping and it also started the sequence of trade bills by which the factor was paid for the cheese so he could pay cash to the farmer. Mr Costard would also have provided the ships' papers for each cargo.

From the cheese prices given in Appendix 2 Table B, it can be seen that there was only a small difference of perhaps ¼d. a lb. between the price at which the Warburtons bought cheese from local farmers and that paid by the Navy in London. If we examine the costs we can see how this arose. One major item was the sea freight. From R. Davis's discussion of the cost of shipping in this period we can estimate this at around £1 a ton.[33] The cheesemonger and factor financed the holding of the cheese from when it left the farm to its final sale. If we estimate this period at four months and reckon that including interest and a fee for their services they would want 10% on their money we get: 4 months at 10% at £30 a ton, equals £1 a ton. The cost of loading and unloading and the paperwork at the Cheshire warehouse and the Cocket Office in London probably totalled around 5s. a ton, which all adds up to £2 5s. a ton or ¼d. a lb. for cheese landed in London as the

Navy received it. Cheese sold retail in London shops would have been more expensive. When the Navy was paying 3.63d. per lb. in 1771, the Warburtons on a visit to London bought 56 lb. at 4d. per lb. and Westminster School paid 4½ d. per lb. for 8½ lb. a week.³⁴

The London cheesemongers bought cheese other than Cheshire. The only attempt to estimate the volumes reaching London from the different sources was made by William Maitland in his monumental *History of London* (1756).³⁵ He tells us he was dissatisfied with the ordinary figures and so made special enquiries of John Newman, 'Receiver of all the freights for the several Masters of Ships concerned in the Trade', who provided the following figures for 1729.

	Tons
Cheshire	5,766
'Thin' from Hull and Gainsborough	1,407
By barge from Newbury and Abingdon	2,375
Suffolk	985
	10,533

We have seen that Cheshire cheese was transported not only from the Dee, the Weaver and the Mersey, but also via the Trent. The uncertainty about how much 'Cheshire' cheese went on the alternative Trent route is one of the obstacles to a full understanding of the volume of cheese going to London. This difficulty is increased by an early eighteenth century technical innovation.

In the seventeenth century Cheshire cheese, like other pressed English cheeses of the period, was made in round moulds 12″–18″ in diameter and 1½″ to 3″ thick (Fig 3). But by 1729 Cheshire had developed larger cheeses that were 5″–8″ thick.³⁶ This was an important improvement because thin cheeses quickly dried out and became hard but a thick cheese ripened with a rich, moist and mellow interior and therefore sold at a higher price. It was more difficult to ensure that all the whey was drained from a thick cheese. It is likely that this development required heavier cheese presses (Fig 4). It may also have been the origin of the process of repeatedly skewering the cheese in the early stages of pressing to ensure that whey was not trapped in the interior, which seems to have been peculiar to Cheshire in the eighteenth century. The timing of this improvement may have coincided with the development of larger herds capable of producing cheeses weighing 30–60 lb. Once the technology of thick cheeses had been mastered

22

Fig 3. A Cheshire dairywoman with her butter churn and thin cheeses, 1689. From the cartouche of Greenvile Collins's map of the River Dee. (I am grateful to Geoffrey Place for telling me about this cartouche.)

Fig 4. This cheese press at Booths Farm, Appleton, may be the only stone press still in its original position. The stone is 3′ 10″ (117 cm) × 2′ 10″ (86 cm) × 2′ 0″ (1 cm) high and weighs about 1½ tons. It was probably installed in the early eighteenth century to press the new 5″ or 6″ thick cheeses.

these large herds could produce one thick cheese instead of two or three thin ones. T. Wedge (1794) says that 60lb. cheeses were 'susceptible of every excellence to be found in Cheshire cheese'.[37]

In contrast, the cheese made in Derbyshire in the valleys of the Dove and the Derwent continued to be made in the old shape. This was the 'thin' cheese that Maitland shows reaching London from Hull and Gainsborough. 'Cheshire' type cheese was also made in north Shropshire. Some of this went to London via the Cheshire ports, but there was an alternative market down the Severn to Worcester, Gloucester and Bristol, where it was consumed. The cheese Maitland lists that came by barge from Newbury and Abingdon was produced in the valleys of the Kennet and the upper Thames. Although only a small part of this area was in Gloucestershire, its brand name in London was Gloucester. Like Cheshire it was a full milk, hard pressed yellow cheese and sold at about the same price. Cheshire had a 'dry loose texture' as it still has today and Gloucester a 'close wax-like texture' similar to modern Cheddar. Gloucester continued to be made in the old thin moulds for longer. When some farmers followed the Cheshire style and made their cheese thicker it became known as Double Gloucester. In the late eighteenth century there was a warehouse for their cheese on the Thames at Buscot near Lechlade.[38] Two other famous cheeses reached London in the eighteenth century in small quantities. Stilton was a luxury cream cheese invented by Mrs Paulet of Wymondham, Leicestershire, and sold originally at the Bell Inn at Stilton on the Great North Road. Cheddar cheese was already famous in the seventeenth century. Only one huge cheese a day was made from the milk of the whole village.[39] These cheeses, therefore, were so scarce that even noblemen complained they could not get one. In the nineteenth century Cheddar was adopted as the brand name of cheese from Somerset.

In 1808, when the whole of Cheshire was organised for cheese production, Holland estimated that about 11,500 tons were made in the county. Probably at least as much was made in the surrounding counties. In 1729 the quantity made would probably have been much less, perhaps around 15,000 rather than 23,000 tons. If 15,000 is correct for 1729 then Maitland's 5,766 tons sent to London was about 38%. The rest was consumed in the north west by a population that liked cheese. At Arley Hall something over a ton a year was eaten in the 1750s and 1760s by about twenty people, which works out at more than 120 lb. each.

V

Productivity improvements and the profits of some farmers

There cannot be much doubt that some farmers who took up cheese production in the second half of the seventeenth century found it very profitable. The speed with which production for the London market was increased from virtually nothing to 2,000 tons—the output of perhaps 20,000 cows—by the 1680s is the strongest evidence for the enthusiasm of farmers for this new type of farming. The steady (whole-sale?) price of Cheshire cheese between 1660 and 1750 at between 2½ d. and 3d. a lb. (£25–£30 a ton, see Appendix 2) must imply increased efficiency. They must have discovered, for example, how to increase the grass in the pastures so it would feed more cows. They may have also found ways to keep the cows in better health during the winter so they yielded more milk in the following summer. I have not found any seventeenth-century indications of such trends but there is a little eighteenth-century evidence.

This comes from a few large farms in the four Arley townships. It is possible to identify the acreage of the farms of four men who died between 1700 and 1720. At his death, Thomas Hatton had twelve cows on his twenty-acre freehold in Appleton and the nearby Yewtree farm of 106 acres which he leased from the Warburtons; this works out at one cow per 10 acres. Richard Key likewise had thirteen on probably 118 acres of the Leicesters' Wethale farm in Aston, which is a ratio of 1:9. Robert Okell had eleven cows on about 100 acres at Garland Hall, Crowley (also 1:9), and Thomas Eaton had fifteen on his eighty-eight acres at Parkmoss, Crowley, but his farm bordered Whitley Reed which provided additional grazing.[40] If the number of acres per cow on these farms is representative there was a substantial improvement from this ratio of about one cow on ten acres to the one cow on 6.5 acres that was the average in Aston and Crowley in the 1760s.[41]

We also get a little evidence about the milk yield per cow. Two farm-ers who died in this period had large farms in Aston by Budworth. William Venables, whose inventory is dated January 1717, owned thirty-eight cows and had four tons of cheese maturing in store. William Yate, whose inventory was made in January 1719, had twenty-one cows and twenty-two other cattle in Aston with 2 tons of cheese and a further fifteen cows and 1½ tons of cheese in Warburton. The only possible place for these two to have been farming on this scale was on the demesne lands of Arley Hall. We can contrast the amount of cheese produced by Venables's and Yate's herds with that produced by Ralph Vernon's in February 1672 and what was usual at the end of the eighteenth century.

TABLE 2 *Output of cheese per cow c. 1671–1719*

Date	Farmer	Cows	Cheese Tons	Output per cow Cwt.
1671	R. Vernon	49	4	1.6
1717	Venables	38	4	2.1
1719	Yate, Aston	21	2	1.9
1719	Yate, Warburton	15	1.5	2.0

Source: Probate Inventories

All these figures show a much lower output per cow than the 2½–3 cwt. per year that is said to have been usual in the second half of the century.[42]

Evidence that dairy farming on these large farms at the end of the seventeenth century and beginning of the eighteenth was highly profitable is provided in probate records. Thomas Eaton's chattels were valued at £487 in 1703 and William Venables's at £421 in 1717. These were large sums and they included no freehold or leasehold land. William Yate's chattels were worth £626 in 1719 and he also had a lease valued at £850. He was the eldest son of John Yate, who, it seems likely, took the first dairying lease of the Warburtons' demesne in the township of Warburton about 1670. He evidently did so well there he was able to train his second son Hamlet in the law and was so friendly with the Warburton family that Hamlet was made steward of the Arley estate at the tender age of twenty-two.[43] Even these rich farmers seem not to have amassed so much as Thomas Clare, who died in 1724. His three-life leasehold farm, Burleyheyes in Appleton, had been enlarged from the original holding by the inclusion of a large adjoining piece of Appleton Moss so that it had 192 acres. Unfortunately his inventory does not specify the number of his cattle but the value of £70 suggests fifteen–twenty cows at £3 each plus young stock. He died in September with £39 worth of the previous year's 'old' cheese (probably about 1½ tons) still in the house as well as £30 worth of new cheese (1⅓ tons?). His chattles were valued at £287 but he had more than £900 in bonds and money as well as leasehold farms in Appleton and High Legh. These examples suggestive of profitable farming may not be typical. In the century 1650–1750 rents in the area remained at an average of around 11s. an acre, so there were evidently not enough farmers making good profits to raise the general level of rents. This may reflect an interesting social change. In the old farming each family consumed almost all it grew, so a good farmer who produced 10% more than average simply lived that much better. By contrast, in the business of dairy farming, a capable tenant could pay a full annual rent and make a profit; a bad one went bankrupt.

VI

Some of the consequences in north western society

Before 1650 the majority of landowners of every class lived on their estates.[44] The major gentry, like the Warburtons, farmed an extensive demesne to support a large establishment at their main house. The demesnes on their other manors were often used to support junior members of the family, such as uncles, brothers and younger sons. Their many tenants on three-life leases provided their cash income. Lesser gentry lived in the same way but more modestly. A home farm supported the family and there might be only a few three-life leasehold tenants. Some of the larger freeholders and three-life leaseholders may have had enough land to supply the local urban market but most of the numerous class of three-life leaseholders consumed all the food they grew.

The first specialist dairy farmers were probably freeholders who managed their own herds. But soon enterprising tenants were taking large farms at full annual rents on the demesnes of gentry who were not resident, or who were minors. The success of these tenancies encouraged resident gentry, like the Warburtons in the 1660s, to let part of their demesnes. It evidently soon became established that tenant dairy farmers were efficient, because a new type of landowner appeared in the market—the investor. An example of the process may be seen in Appleton. The Millington family were small gentry who lived at Green Lane and farmed some sixty acres. They also had three small properties let on lives. In 1667 they bought the adjoining freehold estate of the Watts family (which consisted of a twenty-two acre home farm and three little leaseholds for lives) possibly in order to enlarge their dairy herd. By 1678 they needed money. They mortgaged and soon after sold more than half their estate to James Moss. He was one of the largest woollen cloth merchants in Manchester. He never lived in Appleton; he simply wished to invest surplus money from his business in landed property which through the medium of a specialist dairy farming tenant would pay a good and rising rent. In 1707 he acquired the rest of the Millingtons' estate.[45] James Moss is an early example of a stream of outsiders who bought land in the four townships, so that by the 1740s two-thirds of the freehold land not owned by the Warburtons was owned by non-resident investors.

We have earlier discussed how the three-life leaseholders sold and rented their small farms to each other so that some of them could have viable dairy farms. By the 1740s only about half these leaseholders were working farmers. As the major gentry came to realise that they were leasing land to people who were only letting it on to others and so became increasingly dissatisfied with the financial returns on three-life leases they began to refuse to renew farm leases. As we have seen earlier, many of these three-life leaseholds were not convenient farms. They had been added to by enclosure and by merger with other farms that happened to come on the market so that their lands were often scattered. From about 1750 the Warburtons and other Cheshire gentry not only declined to renew the three-life leases on farms, but also bought up any leases or freeholds that came on the market in order to reorganise the land into sensible units for dairy farming and to let it to tenants at full annual rents. This process had the advantage that it often made the land more valuable than it had been. In this way three-life leasehold farmland had mostly disappeared by 1800 and the great majority of working farmers were tenants either of the major gentry or of investors.

As well as this change in the character of farmers from being landowners to being tenants for seven, fourteen, or twenty-one years paying a full market rent, the change to dairy farming, as we have seen, reduced the number of farming families. The size of farms increased from a typical farm of fifteen-twenty acres to one of more than sixty. This was particularly striking in Crowley, where the thirty to forty units of 1650 were reduced to seventeen by the 1740s and to only thirteen by 1800, and many houses were demolished. In Aston some houses were also taken down but the change was less noticeable because extensive areas like Arley Moss were enclosed and new farming units were created on the demesne. In Appleton there was even more new enclosure in the upland parts so very little demolition seems to have been necessary. Down by the Mersey at Stockton Heath, on the outskirts of Warrington, new occupations seem to have developed as the urban area expanded. At Great Budworth, on the London road, the increased movement of goods and people created a demand for inns and blacksmiths so the old houses were put to new use.

Although rents and wages were both stable in the century 1650–1750 the value of land more than doubled from about £7–£10 an acre in the 1650s to £18–£22 an acre in the 1750s (Appendix 8). This was entirely due to the rate of interest (and hence the net yield that people expected to get from their rents) falling from around 8% in 1650 to 3–4% in the 1740s and 1750s. The steadily rising price of land encouraged the small freeholders to sell out and allow their farms to be merged with others to create larger viable dairy farms. There were quite large numbers of such freeholders in north Cheshire because a number of manors—for example Whitley Lordship, Mobberley and the township of Crowley—had been sold to the tenants in the seventeenth century. The rise in the value of three-life leaseholders was not so large but even so it was often possible to make a small profit on sale. Families were also encouraged to sell their farms by the prospects of investments in new trades. Usually a son was apprenticed and then set up in business, perhaps with the help of a mortgage, before the farm was sold to provide capital to pay off the mortgage or expand the enterprise.

Before 1650 virtually no ships seem to have gone to London from the north west though the occasional ship arrived from London. The overseas trade of Chester and Liverpool typically consisted of a couple of ships a year from Bordeaux or Portugal bringing wine and fruits and one from Norway carrying timber. There was a busy trade taking coal and manufactures such as cloth, shoes and tools to Ireland and receiving back wool, flax yarn, cattle and skins. The local coastal traffic was distributing the imported goods, coal and agricultural produce along the Welsh coast and up to Cumberland.[46] The sailing of fourteen cheese ships in 1664 and the increase of this trade by the 1680s to over fifty ships a year was a major change. Almost more important than the cargoes of cheese going to London were the return cargoes from London. As we have seen above, trade with London was trade with the world. The goods of every continent were available there and the variety of goods that began to arrive in the north west was very great. It would be tedious to attempt to catalogue the diversity of opportunities that this created. Initially no doubt just the wholesaling and retailing of the new goods gave careers to many as apothecaries, grocers, ironmongers and dealers in imported textiles. From there, new businesses were created that used the new goods. These businesses were highly competitive because the north west was a low pay area where wages were between one third and one half of those paid in London.[47] So a complex of commercial and industrial operations developed which cross-fertilised each other to create the conditions for the rapid economic growth that occurred in the second half of the eighteenth century.

VII

Three new documents

Since I wrote the preceding essay three new documents have appeared. The first two are letters,[48] printed below, from a Nantwich cheese-factor to a London cheese-monger in 1705. They illustrate a number of points which have been made in the main text. The factor has bought cheeses on farms at prices between 18s. and 20s. a cwt. (£18–£20 per ton). Because the war is preventing shipment by sea he has sent one load of 125 cheeses weighing 22 cwt (21 lbs average weight) to London in a wagon at a cost of 5s. per cwt. (£5 per ton) thus increasing the cost by nearly 25%. In September 1705 he has bought a consignment of old cheese (i.e. cheese made in the summer of 1704) which is now being weighed (on the farm) before being sent to Shrewsbury. This appears to show that an alternative to carriage in a wagon all the way to London was to ship the cheese on the Severn from Shrewsbury to Gloucester. It then travelled on a shorter wagon journey to the Lechlade area from whence it could go down the Thames with 'Gloucester' cheese.

30

From William Salmon [a cheese factor] to Mr John Moore at his ware-house on Dice Key in Thame Street, London.

Namptwich May 21st 1705

Sir

On the 14th instant I sent per John Holliss 125 Ch[eeses] for 21 ¼ cwt: but is 22 cwt: cost 18s. per cwt at 5s. per cwt [for carriage]. I suppose this load will not be unacceptable to you & if I cann send a loade or 2 more on moderate tearmes suppose by your letter it may be acceptable.

Your last 20 tonns is bott [bought] & shall not be weighed as long as I can handsomly keepe of[f] & it is well bought. If you can please to give further order I am ready & cann buy from 19s. 6d. to 20s. per cwt. & am

Your humble Servant
Wm Salmon

I want business much & wish you would help mee to a good master or 2. I have p[ai]d this poore man John Holliss thirty shillings in part of wagges wch pray deduct out of his money.

The same to the same.

Namptwich Sept 22nd 1705

Sir,

I was drawing up an account of some Ch[eese] sent per land for you but finde some difficulty in findeing per whom its sent & therefore must deffer a few days longer when I hope to make it out plaine.

I have bought some New Ch[eese] for you at ab[ou]t 20s. per cwt. Shall send it per Sallop. unless land carr[iage] come lower than at present. It is 5s. 6d. & 5s. 8d. is given for old ch[eese] per land. Your last bought old ch[eese] is weighing & going into Salop in a little time. I shall give you account of all, meantime, I am

Your humble Servant
Wm Salmon

The third document is a contract for the purchase of a one sixteenth share of the cheese ship *Lively* by Ralph Alan Mould of Newgate St,

London, cheesemonger, in October 1797. The names of the other 23 cheesemongers who shared the ownership of the ship and a description of the ship are set out below. E. J. Hogan has kindly provided some notes on the ship's voyages and its loss in 1802.

Francis Ronalds of Upper Thames Street

Charles Martin
William Smith   of Lower Thames Street

Thomas Bell
Samuel Bostock
Ralph Arderne   of Southwark
Henry Arderne

Roger Mawdsley
Thomas Pearson   of Bishopsgate Street Within

Benjamin Wood, senr
John Strange   of Bishopsgate Street Without
William Strange

George Dean
Nathaniel Whalley   of Aldgate High Street

George Hammond of White chapple

Jasper Homes
Thomas Cuer   of Newgate Street

Caleb Talbot, senr of Smithfield Bar

David Dean of St Johns Street

John Girdler
William Haughton   of St Martins Lane

Francis Weysell of Broad St Bloomsbury

Thomas Wilcox of Broad St Hill

The ship was built by Thomas Walton in Sutton in Holderness, Yorkshire, in 1797. She had two decks, two masts, was 76 ft 2 inches long and 23 ft 4 inches in breadth. Her height between decks was 4 ft 3 inches and she measured 165 tons. She was a square sterned brigantine flush deck with no galley and no head, draft 13 ft. Ralph Mould paid £126 5s. 4d. for a 16th share of the ship and all its equipment, sails, ropes etc. including six 4-pounder guns, so the total value of the ship was about £2,000.

Some movements of the brig. *Lively*, J. Walls, master:

1st June 1799	arrived Liverpool from London
31 Aug 1799	loading at Cotton's wharf, London, for Chester
2 Feb 1800	arrived Liverpool from Plymouth
18 Mar 1800	left Falmouth for London
6 April 1802	arrived Liverpool from London
30 July 1802	reported lost off Carmarthen
	all crew drowned on a voyage from Liverpool to London

NOTES

1. All inventories are in the Cheshire R.O., wills, *supra*, identified by name and date.
2. W. Camden, *Britain*, trans. P. Holland (1610).
3. For example, cheeses sent in 1669 as presents to gentlemen in London who had helped Chester corporation (Chester City R.O., Mayors' files, MF/87/38).
4. P. R. O., Star Chamber Proceedings, STAC. 8/266/24.
5. T. S. Willan, *The inland trade* (1976), pp. 9–11.
6. T. S. Willan, *The English coasting trade 1660–1750* (1936), pp. 84–87, shows 8 cwt. of cheese sent from Chester to London in 1623.
7. There are no other readable Chester coastal port books before 1664. There are no ships from Chester or Liverpool in the extant London books for 1649 or 1651, nor ships to London in the extant books for 1637 and 1641. There is much in Appendix 1 that is not in Willan.
8. P. R. O., E 190/45/6, London coastal for 1650.
9. Rev. Ralph Josselin's diary, R.H.S. Camden Third Series Vol. XV 1908 pp. 45–70
10. Appendix 2.
11. Robert Reyce, *Breviary of Suffolk*, ed. F. Hervey (1902), pp. 39–42.
12. *Samuel Pepys's Diary*, ed. R. C. Latham & W. Mathews, II, (1970), p. 191.
13. Appendix 2.
14. *Pepys's Diary*, I, p. 6.
15. J. R. U. L. M., Warburton Muniments [hereafter WM], boxes 4 & 5 contain leases referring to the new wharf area; the 1753 map of Sutton Weaver is at Arley Hall.

16. Goldsmith's Library, London, University of London broadsides collection, IV, no. 344, and G. Place, *The rise and fall of Parkgate* (C.S. 3rd series, xxxviii, 1994), p. 202.

17. Adrian Henstock, 'Cheese manufacture and marketing in Derbyshire and north Staffordshire, 1670–1870', *Derb. Arch. Jnl*, LXXXIX (1969), pp. 32–46.

18. WM, box 32, folder 7B, Ann Taylor's evidence.

19. E. E. Hoon, *The organisation of the English customs system, 1696–1786* (reprinted Newton Abbott, 1968, with an introduction by R.C. Jarvis), pp. xxi–xxiii.

20. W. Maitland, *History of London* (1756), pp. 758–759. Willan, *English coasting trade*, pp. 84–87 discusses Maitland's figures for butter and cheese, and the port books. Willan was not aware of the cocket ledger so did not know that the port books fail to show a considerable number of the voyages that appear in the cocket ledger. He was also not aware of my Appendix 5 note 2 which gives reasons for believing that the cocket ledger is an understatement, and he had not seen the figures in my Appendix 7 for the cheese passing through the Frodsham warehouse.

21. John Holt, *A general view of the agriculture of the county of Lancaster* (1795), p. 149.

22. Thomas Wedge, *A general view of the agriculture of Cheshire* (1794), reprinted in H. Holland, *A general view of the agriculture of Cheshire* (1808), is the best early account of dairy farming and cheese production. W.B. Mercer, 'Two centuries of Cheshire cheese farming', *Jour. Roy. Agricultural Soc. of England*, XCVIII (1937), adds many details.

23. See *The agrarian history of England and Wales, V, 1640–1750*, ed. J. Thirsk (1984), pt 1, p. 149.

24. Thirsk, *Agrarian history*, V, pt 1, pp. 60, 65–66, 144–150 summarises most of the published sources and gives references.

25. WM, boxes 48–61 for Crowley deeds.

26. WM, box 24, folder 10 for Glover's will.

27. Foster, *Four Cheshire Townships*, appendix 2.12.

28. See note 16 above.

29. See coastal port book for Chester for 1674, and for many later years.

30. Thirsk, *Agrarian history*, V, pt 2, pp. 362–363, describes a dispute amongst the London cheesemongers in 1692 over the attempt of the larger wholesalers to keep control of the trade.

31. Maitland, London, p. 758; *Gentlemen's Magazine*, 1781, p. 94.

32. Henstock, *Derb. Arch. Jnl*, LXXXIX, p. 45. P. R. Edwards, 'The development of dairy farming on the north Shropshire plain in the seventeenth century', *Midland History*, VI (1981), pp. 175–190, for a factor's correspondence with a cheesemonger. Cf. also T.C. Barker & J. R. Harris, *A Merseyside town in the industrial revolution, St Helens 1750–1900* (1954), pp. 92–99 for a grain factor's correspondence.

33. R. Davis, *The rise of the English shipping industry in the seventeenth and eighteenth centuries* (1962), pp. 339–378.

34. WM, vouchers for June 1772; Beveridge, *Prices and wages*, p. 200.

35. Maitland, *London*, p. 752.

36. Richard Bradley, *The country housewife and lady's director 1729* (reprinted, 1980), p. 82.

37. Wedge, in Holland, *Agriculture of Cheshire*, p. 263.
38. *V. C. H. Shropshire*, IV, pp. 119–168; W. Mavor, *General view of the agriculture of Berkshire* (1808), p. 375 for Buscot.
39. W. Marshall, *Rural economy of the Midland counties* (1790), I, for Stilton. D. Defoe, *A tour through the whole island of Great Britain* (1726), for Cheddar.
40. Cheshire R.O., wills of T. Eaton, pr. 1703; T. Hatton, pr. 1703; R. Key, pr. 1705; R. Okell, pr. 1702. WM, rentals in box 2, Tabley papers; boxes 53 & 58 for Okell; and box 48 for Eaton.
41. Appendix 12.
42. Wedge, in Holland, *Agriculture of Cheshire*; Henstock, *Derb. Arch. Jnl*, LXXXIX, p. 37; W. Pitt, History of Staffordshire (1817), p. 67.
43. Foster, *Four Cheshire Townships*, pp. 17–19 or pp. 114–117.
44. WM, boxes 5–7, manor court rolls for 1580–1620 show that most small freeholders and leaseholders were resident.
45. WM, box 63.
46. P.R.O., E 190 (Port Books).
47. E. W. Gilboy, *Wages in eighteenth-century England* (Harvard, 1934), chart 39, p. 220.
48. Cheshire R.O. D5384.

PART TWO

Booths Farm, Appleton
a description of a model
cheese farmstead
built 1686–90

*Archaeology, drawings and
photographs by James Barfoot*

Booths Farm was the smallest of the four large dairy farms created by the re-arrangement and enclosure of lands in Appleton Thorn in about 1690 as described on p. 14 (see Map 2).

The farm buildings, comprising the house the barn and the cow-house/stable, appear to have been erected between 1686 and 1690.[1] Until this period farm buildings had normally been constructed of timber with thatched roofs and the tenants had erected them with timber provided by the Estate. Booths Farm buildings were built of brick by the Estate so their construction marks the beginning of a new phase in estate management. They may have been among the earliest brick farm-buildings to be erected in this part of the country.[2] The first tenant was John Wainwright and he probably had a 21 year lease at the full market rent of £48 p.a.

Fig 5. Booths Farm in 1995.

THE FARM-HOUSE

The design of the house was based on a type that had developed in towns where brick-built houses became increasingly common in the 17th century. With the flues in the side walls this type of house was suitable for a crowded High Street where it would stand between other houses in a terrace. In contrast many earlier houses in the country had had central chimney stacks so that as much of the heat as possible stayed within the house. To enable this town house to be used as a dairy farm-house a large room (GF 5 on plan) was added to the rear (Fig 7). In this room, with its large fireplace at the end, the milk could be warmed and the cheese made and pressed.

Five building phases can be recognised (Fig 8).

Fig 6. The seventeenth century staircase, handrail & balusters at Booths Farm.   Fig 7. The rear addition cheese rooms GF5 & FF5 at Booths Farm.

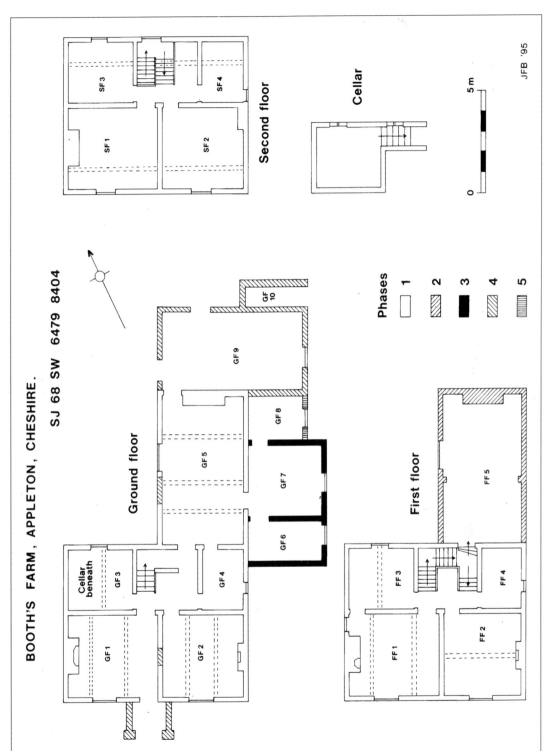

Fig 8. Plan of the house at Booths Farm.

Phase 1

The original brick house was built in English Garden Wall Bond with the walls only a single brick (9 ½″) thick. This thickness of brick wall might have been adequate to keep the weather out in a terrace in a narrow urban street, but in an isolated house on high ground, as at Booths, the internal plaster would have been made damp by driving rain soon after the house was built. So the exterior may have been rendered quite early on to improve the damp-proofing.

The cellar beneath the north west corner, presumably intended for the beer barrels, was built with large sandstone blocks and lit by two stone mullioned windows of three lights in the north wall at ground level. A round-headed arch in the wall at the foot of the stairs suggests that there was originally a hall-passage from the front door to the stairs.

Phase 2

A room (FF 5) was built over the Dairy (GF 5) in Garden Wall Bond. These walls of 9 ½″ bricks are not bonded to the main house. This was

the cheese store-room. It had no fire-place and the only window was on the north wall. The reason why this addition was needed was probably because other rooms were found to be too hot or too cold or not large enough to store the cheese. It became the custom, as noticed on p. 11 above, to keep cheese on the farm for at least a year to allow it to harden so that it would better resist the jolts of the journey to London.

Phase 3

A single storey lean-to of 8 ½″ bricks in Garden Wall Bond was built against the east side of the house forming the two rooms GF 6 and GF 7. GF 6 contained the large cheese press illustrated in Fig. 4, p. 23 and a stone salting table (Fig 9). GF 7 was probably additional dairy space.

Fig 9. The salting table beside the cheese press at Booths Farm.

In the caption to the Cheese Press (Fig 4) it is suggested that its great size is to be associated with the change to 6″ thick cheeses

42

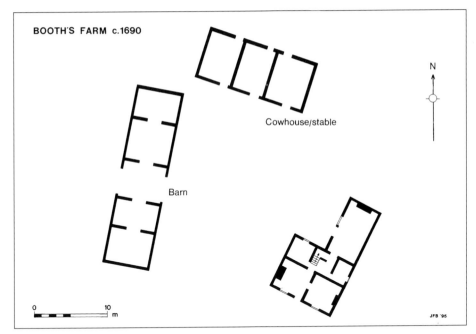

Fig 10. Booths Farm *c.* 1690.

which appears to have occurred before 1729. If this is correct both Phase 2 and Phase 3 can probably be dated to the period 1714–29 when the cheese trade returned to growth and prosperity at the end of the long war with France.

Phase 4
A 19th century wash-house (GF 9) and a privy (GF 10).

Phase 5
A mid 20th century bathroom (GF 8).

Many town houses of this type were built in Cheshire in the 18th century and plenty may still be recognized in 1998. They typically had a large two storey addition at the back or at the side to contain the dairy and cheese store above.

THE BARN (Fig 10)
The Barn was of five bays. The central bay would have been the threshing floor. Doors, the full four metre height of the building, opened into this bay so that a wagon loaded with sheaves of corn could be brought into the barn for unloading. The oats, wheat and barley were brought

straight from the fields and stacked up in each bay. The air passing through the doors and the slits in the brick-work at each end of the barn ensured that the corn sheaves would not rot but remain in good condition for up to two years. The grain was threshed out slowly over the year to provide bread and beer in the house and straw and fodder for the animals.

The size of the barn is nearly double what would have been required to house an 'average' crop if we regard the average township yields on page 64 and in Appendix 10 as usual.[3] Two reasons may be suggested for this. It may have been thought desirable to have sufficient storage space for a bumper crop which would have been nearly twice the 'average' crop.[4] In addition, it may have been the practice to 'carry over' a significant proportion of one year's crop into the next season so as to guard against a crop failure in any year. For example, the last of the crop harvested in the summer of 1690 might not have been threshed until Christmas 1691.[5]

In the 19th century, with better manures and so more grass, the size of dairy herds increased. The southern end of the barn was converted into 2 cow-sheds. This seems to have caused the eastern wall to be rebuilt with smaller bricks. Some use of the barn for cows may have occurred earlier. This change from barn to cow-house will have been assisted by the introduction of steam driven threshing machines in the 19th century. In the 20th century the whole barn was used as a cow-house with straw storage over.

THE COW-HOUSE/STABLE (Fig 10)

The two western rooms were designed for the cows. Each had space for 6 cows so together they provided for ten or twelve cows. We have seen earlier (see p. 25) that this was likely to have been the number of cows on a farm of this size around 1690. By the middle of the 18th century there may have been 16 cows on the farm (see Appendix 12) and more space, perhaps in the barn, must have been found for them. The eastern room, which is larger, was the stable. In the loft over all three was kept the straw after it had been threshed. This provided the bedding for the animals and also part of their winter feed. Perhaps room in the stable was found for the young calves.

This building was part of the boundary of the fields to the north so that the animals could go directly to their pastures from the doorways on the north side.

Other facilities in the farmstead, such as a cart shed, pigsty and hen roost, were probably originally provided by timber lean-to structures attached to these buildings. These have been removed or replaced by later additions.[6]

NOTES

1. The evidence that the dairy farms in Appleton were created between 1686 and 1690 is as follows. Mr. Jennings' lease to Hillside in Lower Appleton was dated 1686 (WM Box 62). A lease to Thomas Hatton probably for Yewtree was made in 1686 and Peter Clare's lease to Burleyheyes was made in 1690 (WM Box 1 h). Old Farm & Booths Farm were let to Wainwright and Walworth on rack rents. They paid rents of £48 p.a. and £50 p.a. in the 1740s. As the rents of dairy farms in this part of Cheshire were stable between 1660 and 1750 they were probably paying the same rents in 1690. Sir George Warburton, 1st Bart. of Arley, gave a life lease to these two farms to his fourth son, Robert, in order to provide him with an income. Robert appears in the 1691 rental (which is the first of a group which survive) paying £5 0s 6d p.a. for these two farms (WM Box 2). John Wainwright attended the Manor Court from 1687 (WM Box 9). The Walworth family remained at Old Farm paying £50 p.a. till the early 1770s probably completing four 21-year leases. When Sir Peter Warburton, 2nd Bart., settled the Estate in 1697 five large farms in Appleton were among a group of farms which were not allowed to be let on leases for lives (WM Box 38). Two of these Appleton farms were those leased to Wainwright and Walworth.
2. This farmstead can usefully be compared with those described by Holland, 1808, pp 83–85. Broomfields, Appleton, of which he gives a plan, was a farm of about 187 acres between 1792 and 1813.
3. The capacity of the four corn bays (Fig 10) was about 450 cu. metres (17.5 × 6 × 4m plus roof space). At the average township yields the volume of straw per acre would be approx. 12.5 cu metres (see, for example, Primrose McConnell, Agricultural Notebook, 1922, pp. 195–9 for volumes of straw per bushel). The leases of these rack rented dairy farms normally restricted the amount of the land that could be ploughed to 25% (see WM Box 31 for these leases & Box 71 for a 1716 example). Normally about one fifth of the arable land would be fallow each year, so on Booths Farm crops were probably usually grown on around 19 acres. Thus, 19 × 12.5 = 237.5 cu metres for an 'average' crop. The capacity of the Booths Farm barn at about 4.5 cu metres for each of its 98 acres was not dissimilar from that of the Broomfields barn (evidently built in the late 18th century) which had about 4 cu metres for each of its 187 acres.
4. Holland, 1808, pp. 133–8.
5. The Arley Hall Granary Books (WM Box 22) have a number of examples. In the most extreme case wheat harvested in 1771 was not threshed until June 1773.
6. The survey archive will be deposited in the Cheshire Record Office.

PART THREE

Farming around Arley
in the mid eighteenth
century

I

Introduction

Part Three looks at the detailed practice of Cheshire agriculture and the farms that produced the cheese which was shipped to London. The first two sections describe Sir Peter Warburton's farm at Arley Hall in the 1750s. The archives preserved at Arley include not only farm accounts showing the crops and their value in each field each year but also timesheets which describe the work that each man did in every week in the year.

The farm at Arley was not in fact producing cheese either for the market or for the household. Such a large community consumed the entire output of its 12 cows as milk, cream and butter, and bought cheese from other local farmers. Half the land was in arable cultivation, a considerably higher proportion than on any of the other farms described. Again, all the produce of these fields was consumed on the place. In addition to providing grain for the humans and the working farm animals a gentleman's farm had to support a number of coach horses and riding horses.

The farm was run by Thomas Done, Sir Peter's accountant/manager and the farm foreman, Peter Swinton. Both these young men were probably the sons of local dairy farmers and had therefore learnt their farming 'on the job' at home. Done's family had been rich enough to give him the education that qualified him as an accountant. He married Lady Elizabeth Warburton's maid, Katherine Shuttleworth, in 1751 when his salary was increased to £40 per annum. In 1754 he left Arley to become accountant/manager for Sir Peter Leicester at Tabley Hall. Peter Swinton's family were probably not so well off as the Dones. However it is likely that they provided at least some part of the capital which he needed to start his successful career as the tenant of one of the Warburtons' cheese producing farms (described in Section V below). With these two men in charge we can be confident that the the records describe what was thought to be the best practice of the period.

In Section IV we discover exactly how other farms in the area were managed. This information comes from another group of unusual archives – the detailed tithe returns for three townships for a number of years in the 1750s and 1760s. These townships covered an area of over

5,000 acres and included more than 60 farms of over 5 acres so they provide a good sample of farming practices in north Cheshire.

The fifth section combines the details of the Arley farm with the information in the tithe returns in an attempt to reconstruct a 'typical Cheshire Cheese farm' in the mid eighteenth century. The amount of land used for each crop is described and the costs and profits from each are estimated. The amount of time the farm workers would have spent on each task is sketched and the analysis ends with estimates of the capital required on the farm and the cash flow available to reward that capital.

Section VI is about the people who lived in the country and worked on the land. A series of short biographies of different families attempts to show the diversity of people engaged in farming and the wide range of fortunes that could occur to them during their working lives.

II

The Arley Hall farm and the farm workers in 1750

On 13th January 1750 a young man called Thomas Done began work as Accountant/Manager for Sir Peter Warburton, 4th Bt, at Arley Hall. In a great leatherbound ledger 16″ × 12″ he started recording all the money he received and paid and for every payment he provided a voucher, either the receipted invoice or a receipt he wrote himself.[1] For the wages of the farm workers he wrote out a timesheet every week describing what they had done. These time sheets from 13th January 1750 to 7th September 1751 have survived and only seven from the autumn of 1750 are missing. Thomas Done also described the crop in each field each year and its value on the ground just before it was harvested. With these two sources of information, it is possible to see how Cheshire farming was carried on in the 1750s, how long each operation took, how much it cost, and what the results were worth.

Map 4 shows the land around Arley Hall that Sir Peter was farming and the crop in each field in 1750. This is summarised in Table 3.

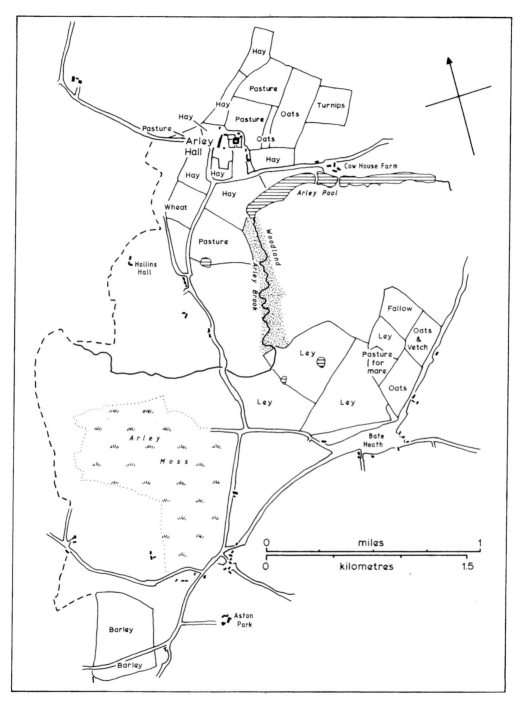

Map 4. The Arley Hall Farm in 1750.

TABLE 3 *Land Use on Arley Hall Farm 1750*

	Acres
Pasture for horses and cows	52.5
Hay for horses and cows	42.0
Arable	109.0
	203.5
Land usually let as a 'ley' but grazed by sheep in 1750	109.5
Total	313.0[2]

Three large fields (44 acres) near the Hall were used to graze the cows and horses. A little field beside the yard fed the calves and a larger, but secluded close to the south held the breeding mare and three colts. In all this made 52.5 acres which fed Sir Peter's livestock from May to November, or even up to Christmas in a mild year. Their winter rations were provided by six fields comprising 42 acres which were mown for hay.

Four fields to the south, making a total of 109.5 acres, were grazed in 1750 by sheep. This was a departure from the normal practice. For many years the Warburtons had set aside this part of their Park at Arley for a Ley where local people could pasture their cattle for the summer on payment of a fee.

However, in September 1749, the cattle plague which had been raging for several years in the south of England arrived in the area.[3] This plague, which was almost certainly foot and mouth disease, was dealt with, as in our own generation, by slaughtering affected animals. This policy soon reduced the cattle population of the area to less than half its usual numbers. By February 1750 it was clear to Thomas Done that there would be few customers for the Ley so he bought 60 sheep at Chester Fair. In April he bought 170 more from Thomas Dutton of Great Budworth. They shared the 109 acres all summer with three cows, two heifers and a calf.

The remaining 109 acres were arable.

TABLE 4 *Arley Hall Farm Crops 1750*

Crop	Acres
Wheat	10.6
Oats	34.7
Barley	38.0
Turnips	11.3
Vetch and oats	6.0
Fallow	8.5
	109.0

Here too the cattle plague had cast its shadow. The 38 acres where barley was grown in 1750 would normally have been let for pasture; the barley would have been where the turnips were grown and the turnips would not have been planted. Apart from these extraordinary items the rest of the farm arrangements were dictated by the Warburton family's way of life.

Sir Peter kept six coach horses (Fig 11), some six to eight riding horses and four farm horses. We even know their names from the invoices of the blacksmith who shod them:

William Beswick's invoice receipted 2 February 1749/50

	£	s	d
for 8 new shews [shoes] of Ball and ye gre [y] Hors [e] 02 s and 4 removes of Brisk 5 d	00	02	5

To look after the coach horses there was a coachman, paid £10 p.a., and the groom, on £6 p.a., cared for the riding horses. The postillion, a boy

Fig 11. A coach and six with postillion, coachman and rider.

paid only £3 p.a., probably had to take orders from both of them. The four farm horses were the responsibility of the farm foreman, known as the husbandman, Peter Swinton, who was paid £6 p.a. All these people were unmarried and lived and ate at Arley Hall.[4] There were usually a bull or two and about a dozen cows which were milked by Elizabeth Pears, the dairymaid, who also lived in the Hall on a salary of £3 p.a. In order for the cows to provide milk and butter all the year round their calving was arranged to happen in succession, one every month.[5] Elizabeth did not make cheese but she did make butter. Milking ten or twelve cows was reckoned as much as one person could do.

The rest of the farming activities were carried on by labourers, who were paid by the day, not by the year. There were nine regular men in 1750 of whom two worked all the time in the gardens. Other men worked for shorter periods particularly in the busy summer season. These men were normally married and lived out; they were paid 8d. a day in winter and 10d. in summer. In summer a day was 6 am to 6 pm with breaks for meals, in winter it was dawn to dusk. For six days a week this made £11 14s. 0d. a year. They were assisted by two or three boys. These boys usually started work about the age of ten when their wages were 3d. or 4d. a day and were slowly advanced to adult rates. In the summer the staff was augmented by women who had specialist jobs and were paid 5d. a day.

The weekly timesheets show the pattern of the labourer's life. (Fig 12) In winter there were usually two teams ploughing. Each consisted of a man holding the plough which was pulled by two horses in line driven by a boy. The ploughs themselves were made of wood by Thomas Cooper, wheelwright.

Thos Cooper's invoice receipted 14 March 1749/50

March the 5	£	s	d
Work done for Sr Peter Warburton Bart by me Thos Cooper			
for Braking timber up trees 7 days [myself]	0	7	0
one man 8 days at tenpence a day		6	8
one prentes 7 days and a have at fore pence a day		2	6
for repairing sum plows		1	10
March the 13 for making 2 plows and throking one		2	10
	1	0	10

54

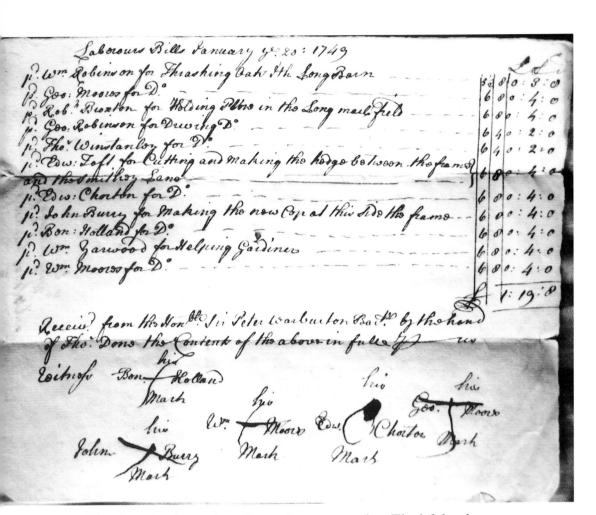

Labourers Bills January ye 20: 1749

pd. Wm. Robinson for Thrashing Oak ith Long Barn — 6 | 8 | 0 : 3 : 0
pd. Geo: Moores for Do. — 6 | 8 | 0 : 4 : 0
pd. Robt. Buxton for Holding Plow in the Long marl field — 6 | 8 | 0 : 4 : 0
pd. Geo: Robinson for Druving Do. — 6 | 4 | 0 : 2 : 0
pd. Thos. Winstanley for Do. — 6 | 4 | 0 : 2 : 0
pd. Edw: Toft for Cutting and making the hedge between the frame and the Smithey Lane — 6 | 8 | 0 : 4 : 0
pd. Edw: Chorlton for Do. — 6 | 8 | 0 : 4 : 0
pd. John Burry for making the new Cop at this Side the frame — 6 | 8 | 0 : 4 : 0
pd. Ben: Holland for Do. — 6 | 8 | 0 : 4 : 0
pd. Wm. Garwood for Helping Gardiner — 6 | 8 | 0 : 4 : 0
pd. Wm. Moores for Do. — 6 | 8 | 0 : 4 : 0

£ 1 : 19 : 8

Receivd. from the Honble. Sir Peter Warburton Bart. by the hand of Tho: Done the Content of the above in full

Witness — Ben: his + Holland Mark

John his + Burry Mark

Wm. his + Moore Mark

Edw: his + C Chorlton Mark

Geo: his + Moore Mark

Fig 12. Timesheet for the week ending 20 January 1749/50. The left hand column shows the number of days worked (usually 6), the next column is the rate of 8d. a day making 4s. od. for the week for a man. The two boys driving the plough horses only got 4d. a day. The second plough was being 'held' by the foreman, Peter Swinton.

Fig 13. Ploughing with two horses.

The iron coulter, share and mould board were probably of Rotherham type[6] and were made, or at least kept in repair and the edges steeled by William Beswick, the blacksmith.

William Beswick's invoice receipted 2 February 1749/50

	£	s	d
For a new Suck Mould 11 pound 02s			
and makeing it and steeling poynt 7d	0	2	7
for leing and steeling a Suck and coulter	0	1	0

As the Arley land is heavy clay it seems usually to have been ploughed into wide rounded ridges (Fig 14). The valleys between were known as gutters and were carefully shaped by hand so as to try and drain the land to the ditches on the edges of the fields.[7]

Of the other five labourers, two or three were usually hedging and ditching and the others were threshing in the barns. This must have been the most wearing and repetitive activity in farming. The technology had remained unchanged for many centuries (Fig 15 a, b). In a good day's work a man could thresh four bushels of wheat, or six of barley, or twelve of oats. But could he go on doing it day after day, week after week, all through the winter? The traditional way to motivate the workers was to have the job done on piecework and this is what happened at Arley. First the men threshed a sample of each crop on ordinary day wages so that the yield could be checked, then they were set to do it at 3d. a bushel for wheat, 2d. for barley and 1d. for oats. When Ben Holland and George Moore threshed 887 bushels of barley between 1st November 1750 and 14 February 1751 they earned more than 1s. a day each as compared with the standard wage of 8d. a day.

In the middle of March the women did their first job of the year spreading molehills. This took six of them a whole week despite the fact that the molecatcher regularly caught 300 moles a year. In March also the men dug about an acre of land for potatoes and the women cut the seed potatoes up and planted them. In April and May, as soon as the seed was sown broadcast by the husbandman, the boys were employed keeping the birds off until the seed germinated. In April too the men went over the grassland cutting down the rushes which plagued the heavy Arley land before underground drainage. They probably used a special hodding scythe which removed the crown of the plant as well as the leaves.[8]

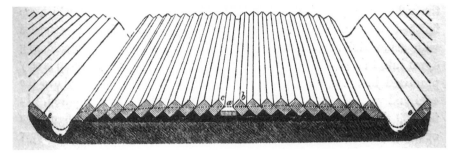

Fig 14. 'Twice gathered up' or 'high-backed' plough land with gutters.

Fig 15. a) Threshing and winnowing in a barn.

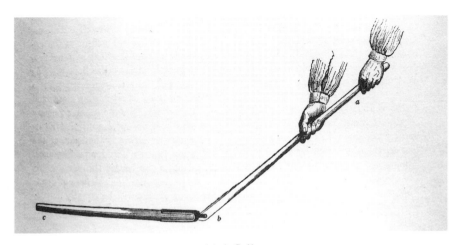

b) A flail.

Fig 16. Carting: the horse-power required varied with the load and the state of the road; (a) cart with two horses; (b) wagon with six horses; (c) wagon, probably loaded with wool, and only one horse.

When the last fields were sown sometime in May there was a little gap in the agricultural programme for the men. Some threshing of wheat for the Hall and oats for the horses went on but there was time for other jobs. Stones were gathered in the fields and potholes in the lanes and yards were repaired. As there was no ploughing for the horses they could be used to move timber, bricks and paving stones for the builders (Fig 16). But in June 1750 the main job that occupied nearly all the men was marling[9] in the Lower Horse Close. This involved four processes. First, the marl was located by boring with an auger. Then the topsoil was removed to expose the marl, a practice known as 'feighing for marl'. Both these jobs were done on day wages. But the next operations of digging out the marl and loading into carts and spreading it over the field were done, like threshing, by the regular staff but at contract prices: 8s. a rood (64 cubic yards) for digging, 9s. for carting and 1s. 8d. for setting. They dug just over 19 roods. At about 80 tons a rood it weighed over 1500 tons – a lot of material to move with a spade!

All through June the women were weeding the corn. As soon as the men had finished marling they began to mow the hay. Again this was work done on contract at about 1s. 3d. an acre. We know the men expected to do more than an acre a day each because, if the area was not measured, they charged 1s. 4d. a day. The Arley team were apparently particularly skilled or else they were the only local team because they were away from regular work, presumably mowing, for 118 man days in the summer of 1750 of which only 37 man days were spent on the Arley mowing. No doubt they were delighted to do another 71 man days at 1s. 4d. instead of 10d. a day.

The men's part in the hay-making was much less than that of the women who 'tented' the hay, that is spread it to dry, turned it and raked it up. Three hundred and twenty two woman-days were spent on the 44 acres. As many as thirteen women took part which was almost certainly all the wives and daughters who could be found. The men who were not mowing, assisted by the boys, loaded the hay into wagons and carried it to the yard where they stacked it in ricks. They then loaded up the muck carts in the yard and started spreading the dung on all the meadows that had been cut for hay.

When the corn harvest was near the boys were sent into the fields to keep the pigeons off the ripening grain. In 1750 the harvest was early and they started shearing and reaping on the 6th August, whereas in 1751 they didn't begin till 27th. The men reaped and both men and

Fig 17. A scythe for mowing or reaping.

Fig 18. Two men mowing hay at top and three women turning and stacking it.

60

Fig 19. Making a stack or rick of hay or corn.

women sheared (Fig 20 a, b, c, d). The corn was bound into sheaves, stooked and when it was dry, loaded onto wagons and carried to the barns. Everyone joined in. William Yarwood stopped gardening; the coachman, the groom and the postillion brought their horses to help cart it home. Unlike the hay which was mown by contract and tented by the women at 5d. a day, all the adults, male and female alike, were paid 10d. a day for the corn harvest. Only one extra woman and a girl appeared to earn the double money. Everyone else in the area was trying to get their harvest in but five more men and a boy were found to help at Arley for a few days.

As soon as they could be spared from harvesting one team began ploughing the fallow so as to sow next year's winter wheat. When the other team became free in October they were both employed carting dung onto the grassland. The harvest was no sooner in the barn than the eternal drudge of threshing began again. As the harvest had been early in 1750 the workers had some time in the autumn to tidy up the yards. While the ground was still hard they carted sand, bricks and timber for the builders. But as winter set in and the roads became wet and soft they settled into the routine with which we began: those who were not threshing or ploughing were clearing the ditches and mending the fences.

Fig 20. a) three men reaping corn with scythes; three women tying up sheaves; raking up and forming stooks;   b) wheat stook of 14 sheaves; c) a sickle;   d) women shearing corn with a sickle.

For the labourers who worked at Arley there was the occasional break from farming. Every week or two one would be sent as a messenger to a nearby town – to Middlewich or Manchester. In 1751 Edward Chorton walked to Okeover in Staffordshire to collect two young breeding mares. One journey recorded in the archive is hard to envisage today. While the Warburtons were at Bath in 1752 Thomas Done visited them. He went on a tour of farms in Hampshire and Dorset and bought a hundred sheep in Dorchester. In early August John Robinson was sent to fetch them. He seems to have walked with his dog the nearly 200 miles there in less than a week. On the way back, driving the sheep before him, he seems not to have managed more than six or seven miles a day to judge from the receipts which record the sales of a few sheep 'that wouldn't travel'. The whole journey took five weeks for which he got paid £1 5s. 0d. His expenses were £10 9s. 11d. of which his own eating and drinking was probably only £1 5s. 0d. and the rest would have been for fields in which to pen the sheep each night.

III

The crops, their cost and how they were consumed

In the last section I described the Arley Hall farm from the viewpoint of its workers. In this I look at the farm as a business, as Thomas Done must have done. What were the costs and profits? Were they farming in the best way?

First the arable land. It is possible to extract from the timesheets and the accounts the costs of each crop. Although the sources are not quite as detailed as one might like, the analysis that follows of the cost per acre of growing wheat presents a reasonable picture.

The profit depended on the yield of grain per acre and the price. The figures for the four years 1750–53 which are detailed in Thomas Done's ledger are set out in Table 6. From other figures in the ledger which are discussed more fully in the next section we know the yields in the whole townships of Aston by Budworth and Great Budworth in 1752 and 1753. The average of the two years is added at the bottom of Table 6.

TABLE 5 *Cost of growing wheat per statute acre 1750/1*

		£	s	d
1 Plough 4 times and harrow as required	4.6 days for a man and a boy and 2 horses at 3s per day		13	10
2 Gutter and sow	0.9 man days at 10d			9
3 Weed and keep birds off	1.3 days boy/woman 4d			5
4 Harvest: shear, bind, stook#	6 days at 10d		5	0
load and cart to barn#	1.5 days at 3s		4	6
5 Thresh and winnow 16 bushels*	3.2d per bushel		4	3
6 Seed: 2 bushels best quality	5s per bushel		10	0
7 Rent: 1 year fallow, 1 year growing	10s per acre per year	1	0	0
Total cost per acre		2	18	9

* Township average see Table 6
\# These figures estimated due to defective timesheets

TABLE 6 *Profitability of wheat grown at Arley Hall 1750–53*

Year	Yield[10] in bushels per acre	Price per bushel s	d	Value of crop per acre less ¹⁄₁₀th for tithe[11] £	s	d	Profit per acre £	s	d
1750	26	4	6	5	4	0	2	5	3
1751	24	4	6	4	16	0	1	17	3
1752	19	4	8	3	18	10	1	0	1
1753	17	5	0	3	15	8		16	11

Gt Budworth and
Aston Townships average

| 1752/3 | 15.8 | 4 | 10 | 3 | 8 | 0 | | 9 | 3 |

The corresponding figures for barley and oats are set out in Appendix 9. All these figures show that all three crops yielded a profit over the Arley Hall costs in all four years both at Arley and on the average township farm. Thomas Done could congratulate himself that his farming was slightly more profitable than the average. But profits were not the point. As we shall see they grew the crops for their own consumption. The only purposes of a profit calculation, if Thomas Done had made one, would have been to show that it was cheaper to grow crops than to buy them.

The standard crop rotation at Arley seems to have been to plough up grass pasture and then:

1st year	oats
2nd year	fallow
3rd year	wheat
4th year	oats or barley
5th year	sow clover and grass seed from the hay in the spring for pasture

There is no evidence that dung was spread on the arable lands. They would appear to have relied on the nutrients in the grass buried by the plough. If a grass field had been marled in the summer, it was usually left for the winter frost to break up the marl and then ploughed for oats in the spring.

The death of so many cows from the cattle plague after September 1749 created a surplus of pasture land. Sir Peter Warburton evidently reacted to this by trying a number of arable experiments. He sowed 11.3 acres with turnips for the sheep he had bought. This was apparently a complete failure. Thomas Done valued the field at less than 5s. an acre which was less than half the rent and no return at all on the cultivation. He also sowed six acres of the fallow field with vetches and oats which probably represented an attempt to see if summer crops of this kind could be grown successfully and then be followed by wheat as some agricultural writers were suggesting. This trial was also apparently a failure as Done's value for the crop was only £1 3s. 4d. an acre and the land was left fallow the next year.

The third experiment was to plough up the clover in the huge 38 acre Westage field and sow it with barley. This produced a good crop, see Appendix 9. It was followed the next summer by peas, beans and vetches which were a rare crop in the area. This was probably a worth-while cattle feed crop which Done valued at £1 16s. 10d. on the ground. But the barley grown in the third year yielded significantly less than that of the first year. They sowed clover and hay seed in the spring to return the land to pasture. Potatoes, which were to become of major importance in the 19th century, were apparently only grown in this area in the 18th century as a garden crop.[12] The cultivation technique was to dung the land and then hand dig. In 1751 three labourers were paid 6d. a rood (64 square yards) to dig 52 roods (about two thirds of an acre) for potatoes and two women were paid 5d. a day for 19 days' work cutting and setting them. Sadly there is no record of the yield but some were sold to neighbours at 1s. a bushel of approximately 90lbs.

Turning from the arable to the grassland we have seen that 109 acres was traditionally reserved for a Ley. This was more a way of renting the land than part of the farming operations. It was a particular help to cottagers who had little land. The only work was to maintain the hedges and ditches and the rent received in 1749 at £60 5s. 8d. was slightly more than 10s. an acre. The charge for individual animals from approximately 1st May to 1st November was £1 for a cow, 13s. 4d. for a heifer and 10s. for a calf which accurately reflected the fact that a cow was reckoned to need two acres of grass for its summer grazing and the normal rent was 10s. an acre. Sir Peter provided a bull whose services were free. The expedient of grazing this land with sheep in 1750 was not a financial success. Done estimated the profit on the sheep sold to a butcher and the value of the wool clip together amounted to £30 15s. 2d. which was only half what the ley usually brought in.

The fifty two and a half acres that were reserved for grazing Sir Peter's livestock were accurately proportioned for the job as Table 7 shows:

TABLE 7 *Approximate allocation of grazing land at Arley Hall 1750*

	Acres
12 cows and 1 bull at 2 acres each	26
say 4 heifers or calves at 1 acre each	4
1 breeding mare	2
3 colts at 1 ⅓ acres	4
16 working horses at 1 acre	16
Total	52

This shows the standard allocation of 2 acres for a cow and less for young animals. The working horses only needed one acre of grazing each because they were also each given a bushel of oats every week. As they were at work most days they were also fed bran, straw and a little hay in their stalls at night.

In the winter the horses continued to be fed a bushel of oats a week which was supplemented by most of the hay from the forty four acres of meadow. The cows that were not in milk would have received only oat or wheat straw but those that calved in winter and were in milk would have needed some hay. After Christmas they were also given a little oats each day. The barley straw made the best bedding but all the straw that was not eaten was used in this way so that nothing that was grown was wasted.

In the same way that the hundred acres of grassland at Arley were all necessary to the support of the animals almost all the grain grown was consumed on the site. The 10.6 acres of wheat produced about 260 bushels. The Warburton household ate about 200 bushels a year in the 1750s and 1760s so as the 1750 crop was particularly good there was a modest surplus. About 20 bushels were required for seed for the 1751 crop but the rest was carried forward in the sense that the labourers were still threshing the last of the 1750 crop after the 1751 crop had arrived in the barn. In other years, when the crop grown at Arley was less successful, they had to buy wheat but clearly the object was to grow enough for their own needs and a modest reserve. It was usual for small amounts to be sold to neighbours.

The same principles applied to the oat crop. The 34.7 acres of oats grown in 1750 produced about 1230 bushels. The 16 working horses with a bushel a week each through the year would have eaten about 840 bushels. The seed required for next year would have been 180 bushels. Of the remaining 210 bushels, the cows may have had 30 to keep them in milk in the winter; the poultry, pigs, ducks and pigeons probably had the same and a few bushels were eaten in the Hall as oatmeal. The remainder provided a reserve to carry forward. The same pattern was followed in the disposal of the barley. Of the 887 bushels that Holland and Moore threshed which was not quite all the crop, 840 were sold to Thomas Harper who malted it at Bate's Mill in Stockton Heath and sold it back to Sir Peter for brewing into beer for the Hall. Fifteen bushels were sold to William Beswick, the blacksmith, and the small remainder to a local dealer. So broadly the whole of the produce of the 203 acres farmed at Arley Hall was also consumed there.

IV

The crops grown and the herds kept in Aston by Budworth and Crowley in the 1750s and 1760s

The Arley Hall farm, therefore, was not a market operation. Unlike most farms it did not have to pay the rent or make a profit. Fortunately, the Warburton archive contains papers which allow us to relate the costs of growing crops as set out earlier to the general pattern of commercial farming in the area.

The tithes of Great Budworth parish were owned by Christ Church, Oxford. Because that institution was so distant, the practice had developed in the 16th and 17th centuries of selling the tithes in each township to a local landowner for cash. Sir Peter Warburton bought the tithes of the townships of Great Budworth, Aston by Budworth and Crowley[13] for a number of years in the 1740s, 50s. and 60s. and some of the detailed schedules survive. (Fig 21a and 21b). In Thomas Done's great ledger are the acreage of each crop grown by every farmer in Aston by Budworth and Great Budworth in 1752 and 1753 and the value of the tithe in the field. The figures for Great Budworth in 1748 have also been preserved. We know from a legal dispute about the tithes[14] that the procedure followed was for every farmer to put aside as tithe the eleventh sheaf of grain as he harvested each field. The local landowner who had bought the tithe had to gather these and cart them to his barn and thresh them. We can check that Done's tithe values assume this procedure because the value of Sir Peter Warburton's tithes in the tithe list is about one eleventh (9%) of Done's valuation of the total crop on the ground in his Arley Hall farm accounts. Appendix 10 shows the acreage, value and yield of each crop grown in these two townships in these years.

Those figures show that of the 2,586 cultivated acres in Aston by Budworth some 5% was used for wheat, 7% for oats and 3% for barley in the years 1752 and 1753. That this was the usual pattern in the township is confirmed by the figures in Appendix 11 which show receipts into the granary at Arley from tithes in Aston and Crowley in 1762–6 compared with the 1752–53 figures. This means that with another 5%

68

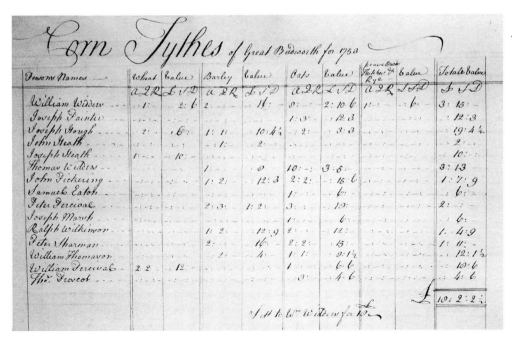

Fig 21. a) The corn tithe of Great Budworth 1753. Note that William &
Thomas Widders, described on pp. 79–80 were the largest farmers. The area
is in Cheshire acres.   b) The cow tithe of Crowley 1766. J. Carter, S. Ryley &
J. Dawson appear on pp.78–9.

which was lying fallow in preparation for the next year's wheat crop, about 20% of the land in the township was arable and the remaining 80% was grassland. In Great Budworth even less of the land was under the plough. More than 90% was grassland in 1748 which probably reflected the demand for grazing and hay for horses on the London road which passed through Budworth. It was probably for the same reason that 60% of the crops they did grow were oats whose principal use was as feed for horses. The effect of the cattle plague is apparent in the jump in the amount of land ploughed up which rose from 70 acres in 1748 to 119 in 1752.

The number of cows which lived off the grassland is set out in Appendix 12 where the number of calves born and barren cows in Aston by Budworth and Crowley for a number of years in the 1750s and 1760s are presented. These figures show that by 1751 the cattle plague had reduced the cow population in Aston to 108. It slowly rose again to a peak of 287 in 1762, before falling back to 205 in 1763 which must have been a bad year for grassland as the price of hay more than doubled to 4s. and 4s. 6d. a cwt during most of the year. In the nine years from 1757 to 1766 the number of acres per cow in Aston varied between 5.4 and 7.6. The pattern was similar in Crowley so we can say that six and a half acres per cow was the usual stocking ratio. This is the same as the figure which emerges from Henry Holland's estimate[15] in 1808 that there were 92,000 cows on 600,000 acres in the whole of Cheshire. It seems therefore that little changed in Cheshire dairies between the 1750s and the end of the century and that Thomas Wedge's classic account of the way in which Cheshire cows were managed and Cheshire cheese was made was also true forty years before he wrote it for the Board of Agriculture in 1794.[16]

The detailed tithe lists give the name of every farmer. The Crowley list always has between 17 and 21 names and many of them are identifiable as the tenants of the 17 to 20 farms listed in *Four Cheshire Townships*, Appendix 2.11. The size of their herds in 1757 range from Joseph Carter's 21 on his 132 acre farm at Crowley Lodge to three small farmers with only three cows each. The largest herd recorded was 25 cows and the average herd was ten. In only four years is a cottager recorded with only one cow; this reflects the rarity of labourer families in Crowley.[17] But in Aston the position was different. Of the 47 names in 1757 only 26 are serious farmers with more than three cows. The largest herds are Peter Percival's 18 cows at the Gore and J Broom's 17 at Litley.[18] But there were 21 smallholders and cottagers with three cows or less. These included not only the Arley farm labourers like Edward Toft and George Moores with one each but craftsmen like Matthew Bushell, clockmaker (2), Thomas Eyes, paviour (1), and Hugh Armstrong, thatcher (1), and also such people as James Birchall, retired freeholder, with two and Isaac Hind, retired labourer, with one.[19] Many of these cattle were evidently pastured on the commons which included the wide grassy lanes because, in 1765, when large parts of Feldy Green, Bate Heath and Arley Moss were enclosed and the lanes were reduced to an even width, the number of smallholders with cows was reduced to six.[20]

V

A typical farm in the 1750s

It may now be sensible to draw all the figures together and assess the position of the average dairy farmer. We have just seen that the average herd was ten cows and that in the whole of Cheshire as well as the area around Arley there was one cow on every six and a half acres, so let us take a farm of 65 acres with ten cows, whose principal product was Cheshire cheese, and whose farmer was a tenant paying a full market rent.

The land would probably have been used like this:

TABLE 8 *Land use on a 'typical' farm*

	Acres
House, yard and garden	1
Wheat 5%	3
Oats 7%	5
Barley 3%	2
Fallow 5% (Total arable 20%)	3
Pasture: 10 cows at 2 acres	20
1 bull at 2 acres	2
5–6 young stock	8
outlet for cattle	3
2 horses	3
Hay	15
Total	65

The costs of growing crops on Arley Hall farm in 1750 and 1751 have already been set out in Table 5 and Appendix 9.

Here I use the same timesheets and accounts to analyse the costs associated with the grassland.

TABLE 9 *Cost of maintaining grassland 1750–51*

		Per statute acre	
		s	d
Hedging and ditching in winter	1.3 days man at 8d		10
Spread molehills, cut rushes	0.5 days man at 10d		5
load, cart and spread muck in summer	1.3 days boy/women at 5d		6½
	Total per acre	1	9½

TABLE 10 *Cost of hay making 1750–51*

		Per statute acre	
		s	d
Mowing, contract	1s 3d per acre	1	3
Spreading to dry, turning, raking up and loading	6.5 days women at 5d	2	8½
Cart to yard and make rick	1.5 days man and horse 2s	3	0
	Total per acre	6	11½

Using these figures we can now calculate the cost of the 51 acres of grassland which supported our average farmer's herd of cattle.

TABLE 11 *Cost of maintaining the cattle and making cheese*

	£	s	d
Maintaining grassland (Table 9) 51 acres at 1s 9½d	4	11	4½
Haymaking (Table 10) 15 acres at 6s 11½d	5	4	4½
Woman cheesemaker – 26 weeks at 3s week	3	18	0
Small tithes, 8 calves at 6d and 2 barren cows at 3d		4	6
Rent of 51 acres at 10s	25	10	0
	39	8	3
Less the grass and hay consumed by two horses say £2 each	4	0	0
Total cost of maintaining cattle	35	8	3

In the 1750s a common price for cheese was 24 shillings per cwt (2.4d lb). Taking this price and adopting Wedge's view that the average annual output of cheese was 2½ cwt per cow, the value of the cheese produced by our typical farmer was £30 (2½ × 10 × £1 4s. 0d.). In addition to this there would have been sales of cattle. Wedge tells us that most calves were sold and this was certainly the Arley Hall practice. The few calves that were reared either replaced old cows which were then sold or were themselves sold as in calf heifers. The prices at which cattle were bought and sold at Arley 1750/90 are set out in Appendix 13. Perhaps a reasonable view of our farmer's sales would be 6 calves at 10s. each and two old cows at £3 10s. 0d. each making a total of £10.

This makes total sales from the cattle of £40 (cheese £30, animals £10) so that this part of the farming business shows a profit of £4 11s. 9d. (£40 less £35 8s. 3d.). We can therefore summarise the profits of the farm:

TABLE 12 *Profits of typical farm in the 1750s*

		£	s	d
Wheat, 3 acres as Township average (table 6)				
at 9s 3 d acre		1	7	9
Oats, 5 acres " " " (Appendix 9, Table B)				
at 3s 2d acre			15	10
Barley, 2 acres " " " (Appendix 9, Table D)				
at 6s 11d acre			13	10
Cattle, cheese sales	£30			
animal sales	10			
	40			
Less costs (Table 11)	35 – 8 – 3	4	11	9
Total profit		7	9	2

This may seem a modest profit but remember that it is struck after providing for all the farmer's expenses; a standard wage for all the farm workers, the rent and all other costs including the horses. However, one should not regard the profit figure as a true guide to the profitability of Cheshire farming. The costs as extracted from the Arley accounts give a reasonable picture of how a profit could be made but tell us nothing about the crucially important yield of milk per cow.[21]

To achieve a full understanding of our tenant farmer's position we need to look at it in three more ways. Firstly we will look at the labour requirements of the farm; then we will do a simple cash flow analysis; finally we shall attempt to set out the capital needed.

Appendix 14 sets out the man-days spent on the various farming operations based on the evidence of the Arley timesheets. This shows that a man and a boy working all the year and a woman working from April to September would have been able to do all the work on the land. Another woman would have been needed to do the milking and make the cheese. So the likely staff on this farm would have been the tenant farmer and his wife assisted by a boy and a girl. These were either their own children or relations or servants. Almost any four people could have managed. The man and the boy probably had some 38 days spare. These would have occurred between mid-April when all the crops were sown and mid-June when haymaking began and in the autumn between the end of harvest in early October and Christmas. One job that was done at Arley and by many other farmers was to dig and spread marl as described earlier on page 59. At the prices given on page 59 our man and boy with their horses might have marled a couple of acres in May. It was probably the practice to marl each field about once every thirty years.

This spare time also offered the farmer the possibility of increasing his cash income. He could hire himself, or his boy, and his horses out for 'teamwork' as it was called. For example, Sir Peter Warburton used to contract with several local farmers every summer to bring about a hundred tons of coal from the St Helens coalfield to Arley, for which he paid 9s. 2d. a ton in 1750. This was a journey of twelve to sixteen miles each way and evidently took two or three days. Two horses could draw a cart loaded with a ton if the roads were dry and hard, so our farmer could have made at least 3s. a day for this work. He had to fetch his own coal so some 'spare' days were spent on that duty. All kinds of building materials required carriage. Paving stones and lime for mortar often came from the Macclesfield area 25 or 30 miles away. Some ten to twenty farmers around Arley regularly made £5, £10 or even occasionally £20 a year carting for the Estate. It was a regular and important source of income so let us allow our farmer 20 days' 'teamwork' at 3s. a day making £3 in the year.

Now let us turn to the cash flow. In the analysis of the profits on the grain crops it was assumed that all the crops were sold. In practice only a small part was sold. For example, the wheat crop amounted to about 42 bushels. The four people working the farm would have eaten about 7 bushels each per year making 28, six were needed for seed leaving 8 bushels to be sold. Of the oat crop of 121 bushels, the two horses, if they were as well fed as Sir Peter Warburton's, would have eaten nearly

100, and all the rest would have been required for seed. The 40 bushels of barley were normally destined to be made into beer so a tee-total farmer might have made an extra £5 6s. 4d. cash here, but most people regarded beer as part of their ordinary diet so they probably consumed half the crop as beer. The cheese eaten in the house was probably the low quality output made at the beginning and end of the season and other defective cheeses which the factor would not buy. These, plus the milk and butter eaten, were probably not considered part of the 2½ cwts of cheese which the average cow produced. We can summarise our 'average' farmer's cash position:

TABLE 13 *Possible tenant farmer's cash flow 1750–51*

	£	s	d
Sales of grain, wheat £2, Barley £2	4	0	0
Sale of cheese £30	30	0	0
Sale of cattle	10	0	0
Cash earned for teamwork	3	0	0
	47	0	0
Less rent of 65 acres at 10s. acre	32	10	0
Cash remaining	14	10	0

This £14 10s. 0d. was not all profit. The farmer and his family still had to buy their clothes, their coal and other household necessaries. But they had their poultry and their pigs which did not seem to cost them anything and the pleasure of being able to drive to market in their own horse and cart was also of value.

Finally we look at the capital required to operate a farm of this size. A reasonable approximation is set out:

TABLE 14 *Working capital required for 'typical' farm of 65 acres 1750–51*[22]

	£	s	d
Ten cows at £5 each	50	0	0
Six young stock say (see Appendix 13)	11	0	0
Two horses at £5 each	10	0	0
Carts, ploughs and harness, say	6	0	0
Crops, in the barn or in the field, depending on the time of year	35	0	0
Dairy and other equipment	3	0	0
Cheese in stock or cash in hand ready to pay the rent	30	0	0
	£145	0	0

The rate of interest on money lent on mortgage in the area was about 4% in the early 1750s.[23] Our typical farmer would have had to have made a profit well in excess of £6 a year if he was to think that he had made a sensible decision to invest in the risky business of farming rather than in the security of a mortgage. In the next section some farmers who made their fortunes are described and also others who went bankrupt.

VI

Representative tenant farmers described

If there was an ideal tenant farmer perhaps he was Peter Swinton. In 1750, in his twenties, he was foreman of the farm at Arley Hall. He was paid a salary of £6 a year and lived and ate in the house with the fifteen other staff, eight men and seven women.[24] So many young unmarried people together evidently created an amorous atmosphere because his was the second wedding of the summer when, in September 1751, he married the housemaid Jane Whittle. This romance must have had the approval of the Warburtons because the young couple were given the tenancy of some forty acres attached to Stockton Heath House at £24 a year. They evidently had enough savings to stock it and their farming must have been a success because, in 1758, as part of a reshuffle of farms, they moved to Dingle Farm, Appleton, where they took a 21-year lease of about 66 acres at £48 a year. They had ten children, roughly one every two years, between 1752 and 1775. New enclosures were added to their farm in the 1760s and 1770s and they took a new 21-year lease in 1779 of 108 acres at £77 14s. od. p.a. and spent the rest of their lives there. They remained on good terms with the Warburtons and regularly carted coal and building materials for the Estate.[25]

William Robinson was the tenant of a smaller holding. He first appears in the archives in 1749 as tenant of the Davenport family on a little farm of 16 acres with his house where Smithy Farm, Arley, now stands. He appears as one of the labourers on Arley Hall farm in January 1750. He and Edward Toft were the only two regulars who could sign their own names; all the others just marked. He must have been one of the most skilled and capable labourers because he was the leader of the team which mowed the hay not only at Arley but on a number of other farms in both 1750 and 1751. In the same years he led the party which did threshing on contract. He kept a mare which he hired to Arley on two occasions when they were short of farm horses so it would seem that his wife and children must have kept some farming going on his own land in these years. In 1752 or 1753 he seems to have ceased being a regular farm labourer, but he continued to do contract work. He led teams doing mowing, marling and ditching and he seems to have brewed beer at the Hall every month. He bought 29 measures of potatoes in the spring of 1752 so he may have planted them on an acre or so of his own land that year. In 1754 he was able to rent 17 acres from Arley adjoining his other 16 acres so at last he had a more economic-sized farm. The small tithe lists for Crowley show he had between five and eight cows each year between 1757 and 1765 and one year he sold cheese to Arley Hall. He continued to do brewing and other odd jobs like sweeping 38 chimneys in the Hall with the aid of two boys in November 1761, but these activities diminished as he evidently concentrated on his own farm. Unfortunately, when his landlord sold the freehold in 1766, he disappears from our view.[26]

A man who never arrived at being a farmer was Mark Winstanley. He was born in 1739 and in July 1750, aged eleven, he started work on the Arley Hall farm driving the plough horses at 4d. a day. His rate was raised to 5d. in September 1750 and he worked regularly till at least September 1751 when there is a gap in the records. When next we find him in April 1754, aged 15, he had learnt to read and write and was working at 8d. a day as a carpenter for Sam Pickering who did all the rough carpentry at Arley. Mark's wages were increased in line with his skill to 10d. in December 1754, 1s. in March 1756 and finally to 1s. 2d., which was a fully-skilled man's rate in March 1758. He left Sam Pickering in August 1758. The latter had some disagreement with the Estate in April 1764 when we find Mark Winstanley replaced him as the Arley carpenter. He and his team of two or three other carpenters all charged themselves at 1s. 4d. a day. The same year he bought two new 'lives' in the family's leasehold cottage in Aston (now called Longridge). In 1765 he married and the next year rented eight acres so he could keep a couple of cows. He and his son, born 1768, and two others were still doing all the carpentry on the Estate in 1788 and charging themselves at 1s. 6d. a day. Many farmworkers were still on 1s. a day so at least he could congratulate himself on not having spent his life as a farm labourer.[27]

Moving from the small tenants to the large, Joseph Carter first appears in the 1750s farming at Crowley Lodge. Here he worked 132 acres, worth £85 p.a., as tenant of the Davenport family, merchants of Chorley, (Alderley Edge) Cheshire. When the Davenports sold the freehold in 1766 and he had to leave that farm, Sir Peter Warburton, who had observed that he was a capable farmer, invited him to take a 10-year-lease at £155 a year of 151 acres at Aston Park which included the best land in Aston by Budworth. In 1776 he took a 21 year lease of the same farm at £210 p.a. He brought up his two sons to be farmers and in the 1780s Samuel was the tenant of New Farm, Aston, at £168 p.a. and his brother Peter rented Budworth Heath Farm at £132 p.a. These however were only short tenancies in contrast to the family's stay at Aston Park where they continued until the second half of the nineteenth century.[28]

If Joseph Carter appears to have founded a farming dynasty, it was modest compared with the Beckett family. In 1759 John Beckett took a 21-year-lease at £210 p.a. of the Warburtons' 256 acre Sutton Hall Farm at Sutton Weaver. In the late 1760s Samuel Beckett, possibly brother of John, leased the 301 acre Warburton Park Farm, Warburton, at £250 p.a. In the next generation Allen Beckett, son of John, was manager of the Arley Estate 1776 to 1791 and his brother Thomas ran the Tabley Estate at the same period. Allen moved on to farm at Broomfields, the largest and best farm in Appleton. The layout of his farm buildings are illustrated and commended by Henry Holland. The Becketts continued at Warburton Park well into the 19th century.[29]

These were the successful large tenant farmers. Others were less wise or more unlucky. John Dawson was Hamlet Yate's tenant on the 102 acre Garland Hall Farm in 1749 paying £70 p.a. When Sir Peter Warburton bought the estate from Miss Yate in 1752 he not only offered to keep Dawson as tenant but offered him another forty odd acres of land adjoining at the new rent of £100 p.a. for a total of approximately 150 acres. Evidently Dawson, who was illiterate, had inadequate capital for so large a farm. By October 1755 he still owed £18 8s. 9d. from 1752 as well as all the rent for 1753 and 1754. To prevent Sir Peter seizing his entire farm stock and possessions, he entered into an agreement to leave the farm in the spring of 1756 on the basis that Sir Peter would pay him for his improvements and that he would pay off the remainder of the £318 rent he would then owe by instalments. Two independent farmers valued the improvements at £121 11s. 8d. of which £94 17s. 6d. was for marling and the remainder for ditching and sowing new meadows with clover and rye grass. Dawson had paid off all but £50 by May 1756 and must have paid the remainder and got his business back to solvency because he appears again in Crowley in 1759 with eleven cows, probably as tenant of the Peover School Farm of 57 acres.[30]

When Sir Peter was left with this Garland Hall Farm of 150 acres at the end of 1755, he turned to William Sumner who had just taken the enlarged 300 acre Cowhouses Farm at £150 p.a. Sumner agreed to become a partner with Sam Riley and help finance the latter to farm the 150 acres at Garland Hall at a rent of £100 p.a. They also agreed to pay the £121 11s. 8d. for improvements over seven years. All went well with these arrangements and although William Sumner died in 1761 his widow and children carried on both farms successfully in the 1760s and 1770s. William Sumner, the son, took a new lease of Cowhouses Farm in 1776 at £190 p.a. The same year John Wright took the newly-built New Farm with a large acreage at £315 p.a. Some time about 1780, when records are missing, Wright failed and abandoned the farm so William Sumner added part of it to Cowhouses for an extra rent of £105 p.a. Whether this overstretched him at a time when he was also paying out portions to his younger brothers and sisters we do not know but in January 1783 he went bankrupt without warning. Sir Peter had to forego £305 of rent in order to regain control of the land.[31]

Finally, I describe the two brothers who were the most successful tenant farmers around Arley in the period 1745–1800. As a young man in 1744 William Widders took a 21-year lease of the 62-acre farm and house now called Brownslow House in Great Budworth from Thomas Partington. Sir Peter Warburton bought the freehold in 1749 and so became Widders' landlord. From his first invoice to the Estate in 1750 one can see that he was a capable and enterprising man. Not only had he organised and paid for extensive building repairs and accounted clearly for them but he had sold to Sir Peter some straw, a lock for his boat on Budworth Mere and a barrel of oysters! We have seen that many farmers did carting work in the summer when their horses were not busy on the farm. William Widders, however, went further and exploited his farm's position near the London road to set up a contract carting business. There is no evidence that it was a scheduled service, but his invoices for carriage extend over the next 40 years. After the turnpikes were built he or his employees went to London once or twice a month all through the year. Every year he carried five or ten boxes or hampers up or down for the Warburtons. The business evidently depended on several standard trade journeys. Carting salt from Northwich or Middlewich to the Stafford, Derby, Loughborough areas and returning with malt was one. The Warburtons often bought Widders' malt. Another standard load seems to have been mugs (which was apparently the general term for ceramic bowls and dishes) from the Stoke-on-Trent area to London, returning with East India Company imports like tea, coffee, muslins and silks. But Widders was not just a carrier, he was a business man, almost a merchant. He sold the Warburtons not just malt but a bag of shot, a cask of oil, a pocket of hops and on one occasion £79 16s. 4d. of Trade Bills payable in London. He paid invoices in London, he bought on commission and he went anywhere – Liverpool, Prescot, even Bath. And through it all he continued farming at Brownslow House. Over the years he bought three 3-life leaseholds in Budworth with a total of about 70 acres. He also acquired an 85 acre freehold farm in Stretton so he must have been worth more than £4,000 when he died in 1802.[32]

His brother Thomas probably came to help William on the farm in the 1740s because in 1751 he married Katherine Underwood, the heiress of the next door farm, (16 acres leasehold) now called Brownslow Cottage. He shared the carrier business with his brother and they each presented their own invoices for the parcels they carried. He too was an active farmer. He rented another 40 acres at Arley in the 1750s and bought three leasehold properties in Great Budworth together with 21 acres of land there so that he had control of an economic sized farm. In the 1760s he bought the 76 acre Caldwell's Gate Farm in Crowley for £1,400 so that when he unexpectedly died in 1769, leaving five children, he was worth more than £2,000.[33] For twenty or thirty years from 1750 these two brothers must have been a living example to every youth entering farming in the area that hard work and enterprise could make a man's fortune.

NOTES

1. Thomas Done's ledger, 1750–54, at Arley Hall. Estate accounts, 1750–90, WM (Boxes 19 & 20) and WM vouchers, 1750–90.
2. C. F. Foster, *Four Cheshire Townships*, p. 8 or p. 104, shows the area that Sir Peter

Warburton was occupying at Arley Hall as 393 acres. The difference between this and the farm area was made up of approx. 14 acres of gardens, yards etc. at Arley Hall and 66 acres of woods, mill-pools, rough etc.

3. *The Cattle Plague, 1747–49*, printed by R. E. Egerton-Warburton, 1865–6, from original letters and documents at Arley Hall.

4. A full list of Arley Hall servants in 1750 is printed in Foster, *Four Cheshire Townships*, p. 35 or p. 134.

5. The number of cows and their calving pattern is inferred from the dates and prices at which calves were sold. See Estate accounts and vouchers for a number of years in the 1750s and 1760s in J. R. U. L. M.

6. Joseph Foljambe of Rotheram in Patent 518, 1730, protected his improvements to the shape of all the main plough components. There are no drawings with the patent but these improvements presumably allowed the plough to cut a furrow with less work from the horses. These ploughs became standard in the north of England, see Henry Holland, *General View of the Agriculture of Cheshire*, London, 1808, p. 114. Henry Holland was the son of Dr Peter Holland of Knutsford who was also the uncle of the novelist Elizabeth Gaskell. Henry wrote this book when he was 17 and waiting to go to Edinburgh University. He became physician to Queen Victoria and was made a baronet in 1852.

7. Holland, p. 128.

8. Holland, p. 116.

9. Marl was the subsoil dug out of pits and spread on the fields as fertilizer. It was done all over England and no doubt the nature of the subsoil differed from one area to the next. In Cheshire lime and other nutrients leached out of the topsoil and collected in shallow depressions in the impervious clay. It is thought that the marl that was effective as a fertilizer consisted of these lime rich deposits. There are long descriptions, for example, Holland pp. 221–6 and pp. 348–54, of the qualities to be seen and felt in good marl but as there were no scientific tests the lime content of what was applied must have varied widely. Marling died out in the early 19th century when bonemeal became available.

10. The yields are calculated from the values that Thomas Done attributes to the crops on the ground with an allowance for harvesting costs. No value has been placed on the straw. See also Appendix 10, Notes 1–7.

11. See text p. 68 for a description of how tithes on grain crops were collected. See Appendix 10, Notes 3 and 4 for prices.

12. In a case submitted to counsel by Christ Church, Oxford, in 1770 (their Great Budworth tithe archive) it was said that the farmers in Great Budworth parish alleged that they only grew potatoes in their gardens and gardens did not pay tithe. But Christ Church's Cheshire agent maintained that they were in fact grown in parts of fields.

13. Foster, *Four Cheshire Townships*, for full details of the landowners and farms in the 1740s.

14. Christ Church, Oxford. In the same case referred to in Note 12.

15. Holland, p. 252.

16. Wedge, *Agriculture of Cheshire*, in Holland, pp. 249–286.

17. See Foster, *Four Cheshire Townships*, p. 38 or p. 136.

18. See Appendix 12, note 1, for the exclusion of Arley demesne lands from these lists. There would no doubt have been a larger herd on the 240 acre Cowhouse Farm.

19. See Foster, *Four Cheshire Townships*, index, for more information about all these people.

20. See Foster, *Four Cheshire Townships*, pp. 30–31, Map 2.

21. See Appendix 2 for cheese prices. Henstock, *Derby Arch Jour*, Vol. 89, 1969, quotes Arthur Young who was told in 1771 by a Derbyshire landowner that his herd yielded an average of 3 cwt. W. Pitt, *History of Staffordshire*, 1817, estimates 3 cwt. as average and mentions a farmer who produced more than 5 cwt. See also Mercer, *Jour Roy Agri Soc*, Vol. 98, 1937, who reviews the accounts of a number of farmers from 1767 to the 20th century and shows that keeping cows and making cheese was an art at which a skilled husband and wife team could achieve consistently better yields than inexperienced people.

    A general problem for historians is that farmers whose rent depended on their landlord's estimate of their profits were not likely to tell the landlord's friends how profitable their businesses were.

22. Compare J Wilcoxon of Aston by Budworth's inventory 1755. Also Mercer, see above, and the stock bought by T. Furber 1767.

23. See, for example, WM Boxes 45 and 54.

24. Foster, *Four Cheshire Townships*, p. 35, Table 10.

25. WM Box 18, rentals, Box 21, surveys, vouchers 1757–90.

26. WM Box 53 and vouchers.

27. WM vouchers; Box 10, leasehold; Box 18, rentals. See index to *Four Cheshire Townships* for other information on the Winstanley and Pickering families.

28. WM Box 25, Crowley Lodge valuation; Box 26, Folder 1, letter of 9 Nov. 1766; Box 18, rentals.

29. WM Box 18, rentals; Box 26, letter of 4 Mar 1780. See Holland, p.83.

30. WM Box 58, Garland Hall; Box 18, rentals; Box 24, Folder 6, agreement, 1755; vouchers, small tithes Crowley.

31. WM Box 18, rentals; Box 24, Folder 6, bankruptcy.

32. WM Box 74, deeds of Brownslow House; vouchers; Box 17, old rents; Box 13, leases; Box 52, will.

33. WM Boxes 17 & 18, rentals; Box 13, Leases; vouchers; Boxes 51 & 53, deeds.

CONCLUSION

This book has tried to describe the changes that occurred in the seventeenth and eighteenth centuries in the type of agriculture practised in Cheshire and the surrounding area. It has shown how the number of farmers whose primary object was to produce cheese for London and other markets slowly grew. Eventually it became the business of virtually every farmer. This was a significant change for the north west. It was also a milestone in the development of a national market economy in Britain.

The grain growing areas near London and on the eastern and southern coasts had started to produce for the market in the sixteenth century. As the population of London expanded additional food supplies had to be brought in from further and further afield.[1] The adoption of market farming had brought great changes in these areas. The old medieval farms of fifteen acres or so were quickly swept away in the best grain growing areas and were replaced by large commercial farms sometimes of several hundred acres. Communal grazing lands were enclosed to form new large arable farms and some families had to move off the land to allow these larger units to be created. The widespread social unrest that resulted from this revolution has been the subject of much historical writing.[2] Fortunately other possibilities for employment opened up to help alleviate the crisis. For example London became one of the major ports of Europe and created a huge number of jobs connected with its overseas trade and the businesses and industries that developed from this trade. Other major new employers were the rapidly expanding textile manufacturing industries, for example in Norfolk and Essex.

The north west was catching up with the arable areas in southern and eastern England when it embraced market agriculture not for grain but for cheese. As we have seen, the little medieval farms disappeared into larger units but the changes were smaller and slower than they had been in the arable areas. It seems to have taken about a century from 1650 to 1750 for most of the area to convert to cheese farming and the average farm size was only increased to 65 acres. The gradualness of the change no doubt contributed to the absence of any social protest. But another important factor was the development of other (possibly more attractive) employment in new industries. Foremost among these were the new enterprises in south Lancashire. On the coalfield metal working developed with the manufacture of nails, tools and, more interestingly, watches and clocks.[3] Textile innovations were energetically taken up and the production of fustian – a cloth with a linen warp and a 'thickset' cotton weft that we know as denim or jeans – began early in the 17th century. Variations in the weft and weave, together with improvements in dyeing techniques allowed a steadily increasing range of stripes, checks and prints to be produced which enjoyed growing markets. The adoption of mechanical improvements like the Dutch or engine loom, which produced 20 ribbons simultaneously, contributed to the demand for labour.[4]

By the middle of the 18th century this switch to market farming had created a new social structure in the flat countryside of Cheshire and south Lancashire. But this north western rural society was significantly different from that which market farming had created in arable areas. In the east and south the typical parish had a squire or two who owned a number of large farms in the area. These people were the descendants or successors of the families who had grown rich by creating these farms in the 16th or 17th centuries. They did not usually farm themselves but pursued other careers in Church and State or simply lived on their rents. The farming was done by tenants. These families were full time working managers; they were assisted by a small staff of labourers, hired on annual contracts, who did the ploughing and other routine tasks. In order to get the large grain harvest gathered in the farmers were dependant on short term workers over the harvest period. This seasonal demand for labour led, in many areas, to the encouragement of cottagers with other occupations in textile production. They would leave this work for the harvest season. For example there were many wool-combers and spinners in the villages of East Anglia and Essex; framework knitting was widespread in Leicestershire and Notting-hamshire and pillow lace-making was established in Hertfordshire, Bedfordshire and Buckinghamshire. Precise figures are hard to find but detailed research has been done on the village of Sherington near Newport Pagnell, Buckinghamshire. In 1796 on the 1,762 acres of this parish there were 16 farms and 64 families of cottagers making straw plaited mats and lace.[5]

The structure of rural society in the north west that emerges from this study and my previous book was significantly different. The 'typical' farm in Section V above could have been worked by a single family and most farms were managed in that way. The tenant families might need to employ their neighbours' teenage children if they had no suitable children of their own but very few married labourers were

86

employed except on the home farms of the gentry. A few cheese farms seem to have been worked by their freeholders and more were operated by three-life lease-holders but the majority were run by tenants paying rack rents on 7–21 year leases. Because less than a quarter of the land was arable there was no need for temporary harvest workers. The help of wives and daughters was sufficient to get the hay made and the grain harvest in.

By 1750 a number of manufacturing districts had developed in and around the cheese producing areas. Textile production tended to be on the fringes where the land rose into the Pennines. Most of the others were on the coal-fields or the salt deposits. In the flat country there were some resident gentry whose home farms were worked for them by labourers living in cottages nearby. The rest of the countryside contained some 15 farms on every 1,000 acres and these were occupied and worked by capital owning families. These farmers employed the services of a few craftsmen–blacksmiths, carpenters, thatchers and so on – but only one or two labourers so there were usually only 4 or 5 cottages per 1,000 acres. This was a much richer and better educated rural society than was typical in the arable areas. In the third part of my study of north Cheshire I hope to investigate the origins and development of this unusual rural society.

NOTES

1. F. J. Fisher, *The London Food Market*, Econ. H.R., vol 5, 1935 p.46.
2. E. Kerridge, *The farmers of Old England*, 1973, pp 74–78; W. G. Hoskins, *Essays in Leicestershire History*, 1950, pp 151–183; M. Spufford, *Contrasting Communities*, 1974, p 90; Thirsk, *Agrarian History*, IV & V has a wealth of material on the arable areas and extensive bibliographies.
3. G. H. Tupling, *The early metal trades and the beginnings of engineering in Lancashire*, T.L.C.A.S., vol. 61, 1949, pp 1–34; T. S. Ashton, *An eighteenth century industrialist: Peter Stubs of Warrington*, 1939, reprint. 1961; F. A. Bailey & T. C. Barker, *The seventeenth century origins of watchmaking in south west Lancashire* in J. R. Harris ed. *Liverpool & Merseyside Essays . . .*, 1969.
4. A. P. Wadsworth & J. de L. Mann, *The cotton trade and industrial Lancashire 1600–1780*, 2nd ed. 1965, pp 29–48 & 98–144.
5. Thirsk, *Agrarian History* V, 1, pp 199–202, 247–8, 266–8, 348; S. D. Chapman, *The genesis of the British hosiery industry 1600–1750*, Textile History 3, 1972, pp 7–50; D. L. Wykes, *The origins and development of the Leicestershire hosiery trade*, Textile History 23 (i), 1992, pp 23–4; A. C. Chibnall, *Sherington*, 1965, Table 33, p 201.

APPENDICES

APPENDIX I *Growth of Cheshire cheese trade to London, 1664–1718*

Year	Chester (tons)	Liverpool (tons)	Total (tons)
1664	364*	n/i	364*
1666	n/i	o	n/i
1670	n/i	363*	363*
1674	216*	662	878*
1675	318*	506	824*
1676	700*	406*	1,106*
1678	n/i	722	722*
1679	n/i	1,193	1,193*
1680	805	728*	1,533*
1681	n/i	1,023	1,023*
1682	n/i	1,090	1,090*
1683	1,023	913	1,936
1686	527	910	1,437
1687	755	1,087	1,842
1688	531	1,164	1,695
1689	265	566	831
1713	n/i	1,411	1,411*
1715	n/i	1,392	1,392*
1716	1,089	1,247	2,336
1717	1,395	1,210*	2,605*
1718	1,245	1,441	2,686

*minimum (Port Books defective); n/i = no information

Source: P.R.O., E 190/1337/5; 1338/1, 15; 1339/19, 21; 1340/2–3, 11; 1341/2, 14; 1342/8, 12; 1343/11; 1344/16; 1345/2, 17; 1347/3, 15; 1348/10; 1349/1, 5, 7, 10, 13, 15; 1350/4, 8; 1382/10; 1384/8; 1385/7; 1387/2–3; 1388/7; 1389/8; 1390/8, 11; 1391/5; 1392/3, 5; 1394/1, 10; 1395/13 (Port Books)

APPENDIX 2 *Cheshire cheese prices, 1601–1820*

As 120lbs cheese made one hundred-weight (cwt) the price given, for example, as 2.5 can be read as 2.5d per lb, 2.5s per 12 lbs, 25s per cwt or £25 per ton.

TABLE A 1601–1739

| | | Price paid in | |
| | | Kent | London |
Harvest years	Suffolk cheese	Cheshire cheese	Cheshire cheese
1601–33	2.00		
1635–36	2.50		
1637	2.63		
1642	2.00		
1643	2.25		
1647	4.00		
1648	3.50		
1649	4.00		
1650	3.50		
1652–9	2.37	3.79	
1660–9	2.31	3.66	2.82
1670–9	2.40	3.39	2.85
1680–9	1.96	3.00	2.62
1690–9	2.23	4.00	3.35
1700–9			2.76
1710–19			2.86
1720–9			2.98
1730–9			2.80

Sources: Kent (St Bartholomew's Hospital, Sandwich): W. Beveridge, *Prices and wages in England* (London, 1939), 238–9.

London (St Thomas's Hospital): A. H. John, 'The course of agricultural change, 1660–1760', *Studies in the Industrial Revolution*, ed. L. S. Presswell (London, 1960), 125–55.

NOTES

1. The quantities bought at Sandwich were between 4 lbs and 30 lbs. Those at St Thomas's must have been larger but are not stated.
2. The higher price of Cheshire cheese in the 1690s was due to it being carried overland while shipping was disrupted by war: W. Stout, *Autobiography*, p. 95. Reduced demand after 1700 is suggested not only by the lower price but also by a draft petition of *c.* 1706 asking the Navy to buy more Cheshire cheese: *Cheshire Sheaf* (Jan. 1960), no. 10522.

Harvest year	Navy	Arley	Harvest year	Navy	Arley
1739	2.78		1775	3.35	
1740	3.39		1776	3.27	2.85
1741	3.24		1777	3.63	3.10
1742–3	2.50		1778	3.50	3.60
1744	2.25		1779	2.96	3.10
1745	2.65				
			1780	2.80	
1750		2.20	1781	3.08	
1752		2.80	1782	4.04	
1753		2.60	1783	3.89	
1754		2.40	1784	3.54	
1755	3.00		1785	4.10	
1756	3.00	2.80	1786	4.19	4.20
1757	3.25	3.10	1787	4.31	
1758	3.00	2.80	1788	4.05	3.20
1759	2.50	2.00	1789	4.34	
1760	2.50	2.25	1790	4.74	
1761	2.75	2.45	1791	4.80	4.10
1762		2.90	1792	4.63	
1763	2.94		1793	4.96	
1764	3.45	3.40	1794	4.96	
1765	3.15	3.20	1795	5.01	
1766	3.19	3.05	1796	5.60	
1767	2.81		1797	5.96	
1768	2.88	3.20	1798	5.02	
1769	3.38		1799	6.12	
1770	3.28	3.30	1800–9	6.91	
1771	3.63	3.45			
1772	3.73	3.40	1810–14	7.76	
1773	3.41	3.00	1815–20	6.55	
1774	3.25	2.85			

Sources: Navy victualling, London (annual quantities 22–1,800 tons): Beveridge, *Prices and wages*, pp. 530, 555, 576.

Arley Hall, Cheshire (annual quantities ½–1½ tons): WM vouchers.

APPENDIX 3 *Cheese cargoes to London between 25 June 1685 and 24 June 1689*

PRINCIPAL CHEESEMONGER / Principal Captain	TOTAL TONS / Port	NO. OF CARGOES / No. of voyages	Ship	Max cargo (tons)	*
JOHN EWER	2,741	91			
Thomas Gillam	Ch	12	*Mayflower* (Br)	30	
Nicholas Gillam	Ch	4	*Wiston* (Br)	30	
Richard Gillam	Ch	4			
Henry Thorpe	Li	12	*Ann & Ellen* (Lo) (1685–8)	40	
John Thorpe	Li	2	*Katherine* (Li) (1688–9)	50	
Thomas Thorpe	Li	10	*Endeavour* (Lo)	40	2
William Buck	Li	7	*Benjamin* (Lo) (1685–7)	30	
	Li	4	*Adventure* (Li) (1688–9)	36	1
Tristram Jackson	Li	11	*Joseph & Mary* (Li)	45	
James Myers	Li	5	*Edward & Jane* (La)	30	1
John Myers	Li	5	*Benjamin* (Lo)	30	1
JEREMY IVES	954	39			
William Chantrell	Li	3	*Orangetree* (Li)	20	1
	Li	3	*Industry* (Li)	25	
Lewis Jenkins	Li	5	*Charity* (Li)	25	4
John Littler	Ch	5	*Nightingale* (Ch)	30	2
John Long	Ch	4	*Happy Return* (Br)	30	
RICHARD HALFORD	870	32			
Thomas Shurlock	Li	9	*Elizabeth & Judith* (Li)	31	
William Appleby	Li	4	*Olive Branch* (Li)	25	4
Lewis Jenkins	Li	4	*Charity* (Li)	25	4
Francis Kirkham	Ch	5	*Betty* (Lo)	35	
John Thorpe	Ch	4	*Mary* (Lo)	30	
RICHARD FREEMAN	391	13			
Thomas Hall	Li	10	*Susan* (Lo) (4)	35	
			Batchelor's Habitation (6)		
NATHANIEL HAWES	315	14			
John Falkener	Ch	7	*Prosperous* (Br)	20	
ISAAC HICKMAN	284	12			
James Addison	Li	10	*Adventure* (Lo)	26	1
GEORGE PATTEN	255	11			
Richard Garrett	Ch	8	*Content* (Lo)	25	1
	Li	2			

94

| PRINCIPAL CHEESEMONGER | TOTAL TONS | NO. OF CARGOES | | | |
Principal Captain	Port	No. of voyages	Ship	Max cargo (tons)	*
RICHARD JOYCE	240	10			
John Higginson	Li	6	Deborah & Sarah (Li)	25	
Ralph Higginson	Li	2			
HUMPHREY LEIGH	198	8			
None					
11 OTHERS	365	17			
TOTAL	6,613	247			

Br Brighton; Ch Chester; La Lancaster; Li Liverpool; Lo London

* Final column indicates number of voyages made for other cheesemongers.

Source: P.R.O., E 190/1347/7, 15; 1348/7, 10; 1349/1, 5, 7, 10, 13, 15; 1350/4, 8 (Port Books)

NOTE
About fifty different ships carried cargoes of cheese to London in these four years.

APPENDIX 4 *Cheese merchants and captains, 1713–18*

Merchants	Captains
CHESTER AND LIVERPOOL	
John Brittain	Thomas Thorpe, John Lyon
Thomas Butler	Edward Short, Robert Hanwell
Daniel Cockerill	Francis Cook
John Homer	George Molyneux, Thomas Nevill, John Fisher
William Jenkins	John Cooke, William Jenkins, John Prickett
Richard Mandrell	Nicholas and Francis Cook
Benjamin Myers	Thomas and Stephen Somerset
John Tilley	John and William Stephens
LIVERPOOL	
Thomas Banks	John Lyon
William Garlick	John Somerset
John Greening	Adam Oldfield
Samuel Oldham	Samuel Bell
Joseph Staples	Charles Davies
John Stent	John and James Manesty
CHESTER	
Joseph Elland	Isaac Dove
James Green	Nicholas Cook
Richard King	John Lloyd
William Lee	William Hewitt, Peter Rule

Source: P.R.O., E 190/1382/10; 1384/8; 1385/7; 1387/2–3; 1388/7; 1389/8; 1390/8, 11; 1391/5; 1392/3, 5; 1394/1, 10; 1395/13 (Port Books)

TABLE A: *Principal cheese ships between London and Chester and London and Liverpool, May 1735 to March 1746*

Ship	Master	Burthen	Crew	Approx. No. of Voyages	Dates
Bowes	Samuel Hunter	80	11	26	
Crawford	Thomas Harrison	60	8	22	
Daking	William Taylor	70	7	25	
Edward & Mary	John Littler			13	1738–46
Halsey	John Littler	60	7	17	1735–41
Halsey & Suttle	Charles Howard			7	1742–6*
Homer	Thomas Nevill	90	10	13	1735–9
Jenkins	Nicholas Cook	90	10	16	1735–42
John & Martha	William Calkin	80	10	10	1735–40
Kingfisher	Ambrose Green	70	10	23	
Lamb	Crouch Somerset	80	8	18	
Lyon	John Lyon	100	12	26	
Manchester	F. Cook			22	1738–46†
Mary	Jeremiah Pulford	70	9	20	
Nathaniel	Edward Stone	100	11	21	
Prince William	Andrew Grout	100	11	26	
Sarah	John Lloyd	70	9	20	
Suttle	Charles Howard	100	9	18	1735–42‡
Tarrant	Joseph Young	70	7	14	1735–42
Tilly	Isaac Dove	70	8	9	1735–9
Warrington	F. Cook	30	4	24	1736–46

* Perhaps the same ship;   † 30 tons normal;   ‡ R. Rimer master in 1735

TABLE B *Cheese from Liverpool, Chester, and Hull paying cocket duty in London, 1736–45*

Year	Liverpool (tons)	Chester (tons)	Hull (tons)	Total (tons)	Voyages from Liverpool and Chester
1736	1,203	1,123	1,313	3,639	50
1737	1,614	1,236	1,015	3,865	54
1738	1,399	1,290	1,657	4,346	57
1739	2,123	1,236	1,143	4,502	67
1740	1,577	1,172	1,307	4,056	44
1741	1,361	1,309	1,122	3,792	53
1742	1,774	828	1,018	3,620	43
1743	1,882	944	1,645	4,471	41
1744	1,579	783	1,367	3,729	37
1745	2,051	722	1,632	4,405	42
Total	16,563	10,643	13,219	40,425	488

Addition for May–Dec. 1735 and Jan.–Mar. 1746   47

    535

Sources: Corporation of London Record Office, Cocket Duties on Butter and Cheese, 1735–46; P.R.O., ADM 68/196–8 (London Seamen's Sixpences), for burthen and crews in Table A; W. M. Stern, *Cheese shipped coastwise to London*, Guildhall Miscellanies, iv (4) (1973), for annual totals in Table B (figures for Hull obtained by deducting Liverpool and Chester from the totals).

NOTES

1. Medieval royal charters gave the City of London the right to charge 8d. a ton on all butter and cheese entering London in return for providing weighing equipment. The London cheesemongers unsuccessfully attacked the duty in a number of lawsuits in the 17th and 18th centuries: Corporation of London Record Office, card index *s.v.* Cheese.

2. There are three reasons for believing that the Cocket Book understates the amount of cheese arriving in London. First, no ship is recorded as having made more than twenty-six voyages in nearly eleven years, which is less than 2.4 voyages per year. Ships achieved 3.4 voyages per year in the 1680s, and it was possible to make the round trip in one month (above). Secondly, voyages by the *Lamb* from Liverpool and the *Prince William* from Dublin are recorded in *Lloyd's List* in December 1741 but do not appear in the Cocket Ledger. Thirdly, if these ships were owned by cheesemongers and operated as economically as possible, they would probably have achieved between four and five round trips a year, compared with the Cocket Book figures of between two and two and a half. If the Cocket Book figures for cheese tonnage are doubled it brings them into line with Maitland's figures and those of the Sutton Weaver warehouse in Appendix 7.

3. French privateering affected merchant shipping. For example, no cheese ships reached London between 7 May and 20 October 1744, but thirteen arrived between 16 and 30 November, apparently in a convoy. This interference with shipping caused diversions. For example, the *Prince William* went to Hull in 1744 (the only appearance of an Appendix 5 ship on the east coast), presumably to fetch a cargo diverted to the Trent. In the year to July 1736, 45 of the 57 voyages recorded in the Cocket Ledger were registered for Seamen's Sixpences, but in 1741 only 6 out of 52 voyages were registered. There was apparently no system for ensuring that coastal traffic paid the duty.
4. The earliest surviving Lloyd's Register (1764) lists only two of the ships: Daking and Co.'s *Daking*, 150 tons, built Liverpool 1760, master William Taylor, and Henry Couling's *Nathaniel*, 160 tons, built Liverpool 1764, master William Hunter.

APPENDIX 6 *Cheese merchants and captains, 1735–46*

Merchants	Captains
Anthony Banks	Samuel Hunter
William Banks	E., W., and J. Lyon, Joseph Hill
Samuel Bowes	Crouch Somerset
Daniel Cockerill	Andrew Grout
Abraham Daking	William Taylor
Nathaniel Fields	Edward Stone
Edward Halsey	John Brown, Joseph Young, John Lloyd, John Littler
William Jenkins	Nicholas Cook
Samuel Oldham	Ambrose Green
George Suttle	Charles Howard
John Tilley	Isaac Dove

Source: P. R. O., E 190/1401/10; 1411/1, 9–10 (Port Books, badly kept and not reliable).

APPENDIX 7 *The trade in cheese, 1733–66*

Cheese received into the warehouse at Sutton Weaver by Mr Corbett Costard

Year	Tons	Rent (@ 6d./ton) £ s. d.
1733	715	17. 17. 6.
1734	624	15. 12. 0.
1735	865	21. 12. 6.
1736	1,134	28. 7. 0.
1738	906	22. 13. 0.
1740	1,005	25. 2. 6.
1741	920	23. 0. 0.
1755	1,237	
1756	1,143.5	
1757	1,143.5	
1758	1,202	
1759	1,401	
1760	1,436	
1761	1,405	
1762	1,439	
1763	1,501	
1764	1,184	
1765	1,104	
1766	1,088	

Sources: 1733–41: WM Box 19 (F. Bartolomew account book, 1733–45). The tonnages for 1734–41 are calculated from the rent paid.

1755–66; WM vouchers (C. Costard's analysis of charges, 1756–66). The tonnages for 1756 and 1757 represent half the two-year total of 2,287 tons.

NOTE

T. S. Willan, *Navigation of the River Weaver in the 18th century*, C. S. III, 1951, pp. 39–40, notes that the Navigation records show only *c.* 16 tons of cheese moved in 1732–3 and less in later years.

APPENDIX 8 *Price of freehold land near Arley Hall, 1653–1785*

Year	Present name of farm	Township	Statute acres	Price per acre (£)	Comments
1653	Sandilands	Crowley	33.8	7.4	Sold again 1699
1657	Parkmoss	Crowley	14.8	8.35	Sold again 1694
1657	Caldwells Gate	Crowley	31.7	6.9	
1659	Gravestones	Aston	40.0	9.75	Better land than Crowley
1694	Parkmoss	Crowley	14.8	17.6	Previously sold 1657
1699	Sandilands	Crowley	33.8	17.2	Previously sold 1653
1732	The Lodge	Crowley	59.2	16.0	
1751	Bellfields	Appleton	91.0	18.7	
1752	Parkmoss	Crowley	39.1	22.2	
1752	Garland Hall	Crowley	116.0	19.6	
1753	Hillfoot	Appleton	76.0	20.4	
1759	Galemoss	Crowley	36.0	18.2	
1762	Caldwells Gate	Crowley	79.3	17.6	
1765	The Lodge	Crowley	133.0	18.1	
1766	Sandilands	Crowley	79.3	17.6	
1777	Gravestones	Aston	47.5	36.8	
1780	Firs	Crowley	21.5	33.5	
1785	Greenlane	Appleton	129.6	27.4	

Source: W M, deeds boxes 48–70

TABLE A *Cost of growing oats per statute acre 1750–51*

		£	s	d
1 Plough twice, harrow & roll	2.2 days with team @ 3s		6	7
2 Gutter & sow	0.5 days @ 10d			5
3 Gather stones, weed &	1.2 days women @ 5d			6
keep birds off	1 day boy @ 4d			4
4 Harvest: shear, bind, stook*	5 days @ 10d		4	2
cart to barn*	1.5 days @ 3s		4	6
5 Thresh & winnow 27.3 bushels#	1.2d per bushel		2	9
6 Seed, 4¾ bushels	1s 6d per bushel		7	1
7 Rent, 1 acre for 1 year	10s per acre		10	0
Total cost per acre		1	16	4

* Estimated figures, see Table 5 on p. 64
\# Township average, see Table B below

TABLE B *Profitability of oats grown at Arley Hall 1750–53*

Year	Yield in bushels per acre	Price per bushel		Value of crop per acre less ¹/₁₀th for tithe			Profit per acre	
		s	d	£	s	d	s	d
1750	35.5	1	6	2	7	7	11	3
1751	28	1	6	1	17	4	1	0
1752	32	1	6	2	2	8	6	4
1753	28.5	1	9	2	4	4	8	0
Township's average:								
1752–3	27.3	1	7½	1	19	6	3	2

TABLE C *Cost of growing barley per statute acre 1750–51*

		£	s	d
1 Plough 4 times, harrow & roll	4.8 days with team @ 3s.		14	5
2 Gutter & sow	0.3 days @ 10d.			3
3 Weed & scare birds	0.3 days @ 4d.			1
4 Harvest: shear, stook, bind*	5 days @ 10d.		4	2
cart to barn*	1.5 days @ 3s.		4	6
5 Thresh & winnow 22.4 bushels#	2.2d. per bushel		4	1
6 Seed: 3½ bushels	2s. 6d. per bushel		8	9
7 Rent: 1 acre for 1 year	10s. per acre		10	0
Total cost per acre		2	6	3

* Estimated figures, see Table 5 on p. 64
\# Township average, see Table D below

TABLE D *Profitability of barley grown at Arley Hall 1750–52*

Year	Yield in bushels per acre	Price per bushel		Value of crop per acre less ¹⁄₁₁ for tithe			Profit per acre	
		s	d	£	s	d	s	d
1750	26	2	6	2	17	9	11	6
1751	26	2	6	2	17	9	11	6
1752	22	2	6	2	9	0	2	9
Township's average:								
1752–3	22.4	2	8	2	13	2	6	11

The 4.8 days ploughing for barley may be unusually high. In January 1750 the Estate's two plough teams were busy on other fields so they hired Thomas Broxton and James Walton, two tenant farmers, to start the ploughing in January. Sir Peter Warburton visited them on the job and thought that it was so wet and heavy ploughing the old clover pasture that he ordered each man to be given a pint of ale each day. Thomas Broxton charged 3s. 6d. a day for his team not the usual 3s. a day, perhaps because he used three horses.

APPENDIX 10 *Crops grown in Aston by Budworth and Great Budworth 1748–53*

Crop	Statute acreage (Note 2)	Total crop value (Note 3)	Approx. price per bushel (Note 4)		Yield per acre in bushels (Note 5)	% of land in township (Note 6)
		£	s	d		
ASTON BY BUDWORTH 1752:						
Wheat	136.5	554	4	8	17.4	5.3
Oats	200	448	1	6	29.9	7.7
Barley	98.4	232	2	6	21.5	3.8
						16.8
Fallow, say						5.3
Total arable						22.1
ASTON BY BUDWORTH 1753:						
Wheat	137.5	505	5	0	14.7	5.3
Oats	168.7	492	1	9	25.9	6.5
Barley	62.9	176	2	10	19.7	2.4
						14.2
Fallow, say						5.3
Total arable						19.5
GREAT BUDWORTH 1748						
Wheat	5.3	18	3	9	18.1	0.6
Oats	39.1	87	1	3	35.6	4.8
Barley	25.9	72	2	3	24.7	3.2
						8.6
Fallow, say						0.6
Total arable						9.2
GREAT BUDWORTH 1752						
Wheat	23.8	90	4	8	16.2	3.0
Oats	62.9	151	1	6	32	7.9
Barley	32.3	93	2	6	23	4.0
						14.9
Fallow, say						3.0
Total arable						17.9
GREAT BUDWORTH 1753						
Wheat	9	23	5	0	10.2	1.1
Oats	74.6	165	1	9	25.3	9.3
Barley	27	74	2	10	19.3	3.4
						13.8
Fallow						1.1
Total arable						14.9

NOTES

1. H. Holland, 1808, pp. 134 & 138, gives estimates of grain yields in Cheshire as follows: Wheat 12–30 bushels, probable average 20–22 bushels. Oats 15–40 or 45 bushels, probable average 25–30 bushels.

2. The original has Cheshire acres which were based on an 8 yard pole and so contained 10,240 square yards. These have been converted to statute acres which are based on a 5½ yard pole containing 4,840 square yards.

3. To obtain this value T. Done's figure for the value of the tithe on the ground has been multiplied by eleven because the tithe was an eleventh part of the total crop, see text. To this has been added the cost of harvesting, carting and threshing from Table 5, p. 64 for wheat and Tables A and C in Appendix 9 for oats and barley; that is for wheat, 13s 9d, oats, 11s 5d and barley, 12s 9d per statute acre. I realise that this may overstate the cost of harvesting since the reaping and binding had been done by the farmers. On the other hand, stooking, loading and carting from many small fields all over the township would have been much more costly than from the large fields close to Arley Hall. T. Done's figures may have allowed for this.

4. Prices are usually those at which T. Done bought or sold grain in the autumn. Use has also been made of the weekly prices for grain sold in Manchester in Harrops' Manchester Mercury. The 1748 prices are estimates. The price used affects the yield.

5. Yield is obtained by dividing total crop value by price and by acreage.

6. The author's *Four Cheshire Townships*, Table 3, p.12, gives the total area of farm land in Aston by Budworth as 2,586 acres and in Great Budworth as 800 acres.

7. In addition to the three main crops the tithe lists give the acreage of a composite category – 'Peas, Beans, Vetches, Rye' – as follows:

	statute acres		
	1748	1752	1753
Great Budworth	4	6	nil
Aston by Budworth	nil	1	4

APPENDIX 11 *Tithe corn of Aston and Crowley received into the granary at Arley 1762–66*

In order to compare the figures below with the figures of acreages and yields in Appendix 10 I have set out comparable figures for 1752–53. These figures have been deduced as follows: Aston had 2,586 acres of farmland and Crowley had 1,343 acres as shown in Table 3 of *Four Cheshire Townships* so Aston plus Crowley equals approximately Aston plus 50%. The 1752 Aston wheat acreage was 136.5 and the yield 17.4 bushels so the tithe crop was 1/11th of 2,375 = 216 bushels. Add 50% = 324 bushels.

Year	Area	Tithe in bushels			
		Wheat	*Barley*	*Oats*	*Beans*
1752	Aston + estimate for Crowley	324	288	815	
1753		276	169	596	
1762	Aston & Crowley	264½	353	660	24
1763		293½	130	721½	28
1764		219	313	959	58
1765		167	197	850	18
1766		339	226¾	795½	3½

Source: Granary Books, WM Box 22.

APPENDIX 12 *The cow population of Aston by Budworth and Crowley 1751–66*

TABLE A *Total numbers of calves and cows*

| Year | Aston by Budworth | | | | Crowley | | | |
	calves born	barren cows	total cows	statute acres per cow (Note 1)	calves born	barren cows	total cows	statute acres per cow (Note 2)
1751	72	36	108					
1752	123	29	152	10.3				
1753	133	40	173	9.0				
1757	179	69	248	6.3	154	26	180	7.5
1758	207	49	256	6.1	159	31	190	7.1
1759	222	44	266	5.9	195	19	214	6.3
1760	225	44	269	5.8	210	10	220	6.1
1761	235	52	287	5.4	205	15	220	6.1
1762	225	52	274	5.7	206	15	221	6.1
1763	134	71	205	7.6	181	25	206	6.5
1765	192	35	227	6.8	178	32	210	6.4
1766	180	50	230	6.8	169	22	191	7.1

Source: Small tithe lists, WM vouchers, WM Box 25 and T. Done's ledger.

NOTES
1. The Arley demesne lands [1217 acres less the Gore Farm (192 acres) = 1025 acres] paid a modus of 15s 4d a year in lieu of small tithes so the livestock that pastured there is not included in the above figures. The area paying small tithe was 2,586–1025 = 1561 acres. See *Four Cheshire Townships*, Appendix 2.12, for Arley demesne.
2. Crowley had 1343 acres, see Appendix 11.

TABLE B *Number of owners and size of herds*

Year	*Aston by Budworth*			*Crowley*		
	total number of owners	*size of herd*		*total number of owners*	*size of herd*	
		1–3	*4–24*		*1–2*	*3–24*
1757	47	21	26	17		17
1758	48	22	26	18		18
1759	47	23	24	18		18
1760	45	20	25	19		19
1761	45	22	23	19	1	18
1762	45	22	23	20	2	18
1763	44	23	21	18	1	17
1765	41	18	23	21	1	20
1766	29	6	23	18		18

NOTE

A distorting feature of these figures is that when farms changed hands there were often two cow owners, for example, a widow about to depart whose herd was reduced to two or three and a new farmer arriving with only 3 cows instead of the ten that would normally be on the farm.

Source: WM vouchers

Year	Cow £	s	d		Heifer £	s	d		Calf £	s	d		Bull £	s	d
1750					2	5	9								
1751	5	15	0 fat		2	15	0 large			15	0 price		3	15	0
					2	3	0 small	1	1	1	0 range				
					2	12	6								
					4	5	0 fat								
1752	5	10	0		3	1	0			12	0 at 14 days				
					3	5	0			13	6 price				
								1		4	0 range				
1753	3	10	0							13	0 price				
								1		4	0 range				
1754	6	7	6 red												
1755	3	17	6 old					1		8	0 each		3	3	0
	4	14	0 young								for 7 fat				
1756													5	5	0
1757	8	0	0 fat							5	0 for		9	0	0
										15	9 rearing				
										12	0 for				
								1		10	0 butcher				
1758													6	18	0
1761	6	0	0 milker												
1762	3	5	0 old										6	0	0
1764	3	10	0 old												
1765	4	0	0 old												
1766	4	0	0 old												
1770	8	15	0 in calf heifer												
1771	8	17	0 in calf heifer average										10	0	0
1772	6	0	0 sold to butcher										9	17	6
													yield 912 lb meat		
1773	9	5	0 in calf cow												
1774	8	17	6 in calf heifer												
1777													12	12	0
1779													9	15	0
													yield 914 lb meat		
1781													7	19	2
1782													9	0	0
													yield 934 lb meat		
1790	8	4	6 barren cow sold												

APPENDIX 14 *Man days spent on various farm occupations (Note 1)*

	Man	Boy

Arable 1) Plough etc. Man, boy & 2 horses (Note 2):

	Man	Boy
Wheat 3 acres at 4.6 days = 13.8		
Oats 5 acres at 2.2 days = 11.0		
Barley 2 acres at 4.8 days = 9.6		
34.4	34.4	34.4

2) Handwork

Wheat 3 acres at 0.9 days = 2.7		
Oats 5 acres at 0.5 days = 2.5		
Barley 2 acres at 0.3 days = 0.6		
total man days 5.8		
divide between them	4.0	3.6

3) Thresh

Wheat 48 bushels at 4 per day = 12		
Oats 136 bushels at 12 per day = 11.3		
Barley 42 bushels at 6 per day = 7		
winnow 226 bushels at 40 per day = 5.6		
total man days 35.9		
divide between them	25	22

Hedge & ditch

65 acres at 1.3 man days per acre = 84.5		
divide between them	56	58

Grassland

Cut rushes etc., cart & spread muck,		
51 acres at 1.3 man days per acre = 66.3		
divide between them	44	45

Harvest see below	73	73

Repairs to roads, lanes (Note 4), yards, buildings, say	20	20
Dig for potatoes & other garden work	15	15
Totals	271.4	271

Harvest with the staff at Arley, the times were approx.

	Man	Woman or boy (Note 3)
Hay 15 acres mow 1 acre per day	15	
make 15 × 6½ days		97.5
cart 15 × 1½ days	22.5	
	37.5	97.5

	man	man or woman	boy
Wheat 3 acres shear etc. 3 × 6		18	
cart 3 × 1,5	4.5		4.5
Oats 5 acres shear etc. 5 × 5		25	
cart 5 × 1.5	7.5		7.5
Barley 2 acres shear etc. 2 × 5		10	
cart 2 × 1.5	3		3
	15	53	15

The total number of men/woman/boy days is 218.

Harvesting went on more or less continuously from the 2nd half of June to the 1st half of October; i.e. 15 weeks or 90 working days. Allowing for the need to plough and sow the wheat in late August or September, other urgent jobs and bad weather, a fair approximation would seem to be 73 days each for a man, a boy and a woman (see Note 3). This figure of 73 days is therefore included above in the totals of 271 man/boy days. Some of the Arley labourers worked 6 days a week every week of the year, though many had a day or two off around Christmas and New Year. If we take 310 working days a year our farmer and his boy have some 38 days (310−271) spare on this analysis. At Arley in 1750 this time occurred from mid-April to mid-June when it was used for marling and between harvest and Christmas when it was used for moving building materials and coal and making new gardens.

NOTES

1. The analysis of man days is derived from the Arley timesheets, Jan. 1750–Sep. 1751. At Arley the majority of the work was done by men with the boys' principal function being to drive the plough horses. On a farm with a staff of a man and a boy they would divide the work evenly but a boy is assumed here to do half the amount of work in a day that a man does.
2. See earlier analysis in Table 5, p. 64
3. The woman or girl would have been employed 3 or 4 days a week from April to harvest on jobs like spreading molehills, weeding the corn crops and planting potatoes.
4. There was a statutory obligation to do 5 days' work a year on the roads of the township.

Index

This is an index of people and places. A few other subjects which might be hard to find in the lists of contents, appendices and illustrations are included. Ships mentioned in the text are included in italics. Many more ships are listed on pp. 94, 95, 97.